Introducing Data Communications Protocols

Peter Hardy

PUBLISHED BY NCC PUBLICATIONS

British Library Cataloguing in Publication Data

Hardy, Peter
Introducing data communications protocols.
1. Computer network protocols
I. Title
001.64'25 TK5105.5

ISBN 0-85012-501-4

First published in 1985 by:

NCC Publications, The National Computing Centre Limited, Oxford Road, Manchester M1 7ED, England.

Typeset in 11pt Times Roman by UPS Blackburn Limited, 76-80 Northgate, Blackburn, Lancashire, and printed by Hobbs the Printers of Southampton.

ISBN 0-85012-501-4

Preface

There are three significant changes which are occurring in the use of and requirements for data communications facilities:

a) Increased proliferation of distributed terminal and communicating small computer systems. These often require the exchange of information both between similar devices and between themselves and public computing facilities and information services. These systems will, in many cases, operate independently to large computing systems.

b) Increased requirements to exchange information between devices in large multi-vendor computer environments. This may be as a result of the introduction of multi-vendor equipment procurement policies within organisations or as a result of new requirements to exchange information between computer systems operated by separate organisations.

c) Within organisations, stored information is being seen, increasingly, as a major asset. Within the computer divisions of such organisations efficiency has previously been sought by maximising the utilisation of hardware and software. The recognition of information as a major asset is changing this view such that increased efficiency is sought by maximising the availability and utilisation of the stored information. In order to achieve this it is necessary to be able to exchange this information between a wide variety of devices and applications.

These changes have resulted in a requirement that members of such organisations have an understanding of the principles of operation of different types of data communications protocol. Three levels of requirement have been identified:

— the computer systems designer needs to be aware of the impact on system operation which will result from the use of one protocol vs another;

— the data communications specialist must understand the principles of operation of each protocol that he may encounter, whether in use or as a candidate for a solution to a requirement. Additionally he must be able to follow detailed descriptions of protocol procedures as given by suppliers of systems;

— the user of communicating equipment should understand the responsibilities (for integrity, etc) of the protocols which are being used.

The requirements listed above demand not a thorough knowledge of every, or even any, protocol but an understanding of the structure, capabilities and usage of various types of protocol. This book therefore provides an overview of such procedures, giving details of specific versions as examples rather than precise specifications. It begins in earnest with an introduction to the functions of a protocol.

Acknowledgements

The centre acknowledges with thanks the support provided by the Electronics and Avionics Requirements Board of the Department of Industry for the project from which this publication derives.

Contents

1 Introduction

FUNCTIONS OF PROTOCOLS

In data communications, protocols are the sets of rules which are followed to allow meaningful communications to take place. Information transfer is not a continuous requirement, although the ability to communicate at very short notice often is. Devices will in general have periods when they are communicating (*active*), able to communicate but not doing so (*available*) or not in a state in which they may begin to communicate (*unavailable*). The period during which two or more entities are communicating is known as a *session*.*

The three highest level activities which a protocol must support are:

— initiation of a communications session;

— information transfer;

— termination of a session.

Initiation of a session may involve the transition from an idle state to an available state or the transition from an available state to an active state.

Information transfer is the prime objective for which a session is invoked. The transfer of information must:

— be reliable;

* In the ISO Basic Reference Model for Open Systems Interconnection (OSI) and in some other fields, the term 'session' is taken to mean a particular type of activity period.

— maintain the integrity of the information;

— maintain the confidentiality of the information.

Termination of a session may involve the transition from an active state to an available state or the transition from an available to an idle state.

In order to satisfy the requirements listed above, protocols must provide precise and complete rules. All protocols can be considered to consist of three elements. These elements are:

— syntax;

— semantics;

— behavioural sequence.

The *syntax* of the protocol specifies the size, layout and purpose of the communicated elements. The *semantics* of the protocol specifies the meaning of the control elements of the protocol messages. The *behavioural sequence* of the protocol elements is provided by a combination of the syntax and semantics. The meaning of protocol messages often depends on the messages that have previously passed between the communicating entities. The way in which a message is interpreted is said to depend upon the context in which it is received. This can be illustrated by considering the word 'yes' in a human conversation. Its meaning is normally very precise, but depends upon the 'context' set by the previous message (the question to which it is an answer).

CLASSIFYING PROTOCOLS

Nothing has so far been said about the type of protocol that is being considered, other than that it is a data communications protocol. The reason for this is that the characteristics discussed above apply to all such protocols. The act of communicating information between electronic devices necessarily demands that protocols are followed at a number of distinguishable levels. These levels may be categorised into two groups. The first of these groups is known as *low-level protocols*. These are protocols which are concerned with the communications network itself. The second group, *high-level protocols*, is concerned with the communications between the various software entities of the information processing devices themselves.

Low-Level Protocols

The functions performed by low-level protocols can be further divided into three more catagories:

- physical connection;
- data link;
- network.

The requirement at the *physical connection* is to cater for the dialogue which takes place at the terminal to transmission system interface. This may be via a Data Communications Equipment (DCE) interface such as a modem or directly to the transmission medium as found in some LAN systems. In the case of the modem, the syntax defines such values as the electrical characteristics of the interface, the semantics are the meanings of the signals on each pin, and the behavioural sequence is governed by the relations between signal transitions.

The *data link* requirement is for the transfer of information across pre-established data communications circuits. These circuits may be dedicated (as in the case of a private circuit network) or may be switched (as in the case of PSTN connections), although the data link function does not concern itself with the switching activity. There may be a requirement to control switching of the transmission network. Network control facilities enable information to be passed between the Data Terminal Equipments (DTEs) and the transmission network.

The functions described above can be supplied by a number of different communications systems, eg a private circuit and modems, or a packet switched service. It is desirable that computer systems can have information transported between themselves without having to be modified for each particular transmission system that may be used. Thus computer systems may communicate via a number of different environments without modification. For this purpose a standard information transport mechanism that can provide the bridge between a number of different computer programs or systems and a number of different physical communications networks is desirable. Furthermore, this class of protocol can be charged with the responsibility of providing not only a suitable form of communications circuit but also of utilising these resources efficiently.

High-Level Protocols

The functions performed by the high-level protocols can also be further divided into three categories:

- session;
- presentation;
- application.

The period during which an association exists between two or more entities has been described as a session. The periods during which communications services are made available between an applications program and a user system software element is known as a session, and control of the setting up and disbanding of sessions is necessary.

The information passed between two communicating applications consists of binary digits which may or may not be formatted into bytes or characters. The way in which this information is interpreted is the function of presentation protocols. For example, if the originator sends a string of 1100100 to represent the character 'd' it is of course important that the recipient interprets this as the letter 'd' and not as the hexadecimal number '64'.

The final function is that of the application server. Note that this is an applications software server and not the applications software itself. The transport service described above provided a standard interface between the high-level and low-level functions. In a similar manner the applications server provides a bridge between an applications program and the high-level services.

The grouping of the functional requirements of protocols listed above is extremely important. The more obvious use of such a list is that it enables protocols to be grouped into classes which reflect their functions. The second and indeed much more important use is that it presents a framework for the design of communications systems that cater for all levels of protocol requirements. These systems are called 'network architectures'. The ISO basis for a network architecture follows the seven classes listed above and is referred to as the Basic Reference Model for Open Systems Interconnection (OSI). Other network architectures (such as IBM's SNA) also follow similar patterns of construction.

Individual protocols are concerned with either part of one of these layers (a sublayer), an entire layer, or several layers. It is not usual for a protocol to concern itself with the entire model set out above. In general, protocols only allow communication between similar layers. For instance a protocol may be concerned with the connection of two devices at the physical level or the application level but not between the network control and the data link levels. As such, protocols are referred to as 'peer protocols'. The connections between protocols at adjacent levels are called service access points or interfaces. Figure 1.1 illustrates the main features of each of these layers. Figure 1.2 illustrates the upper and lower layers of protocols.

This book is concerned primarily with the lower three layers of this model, the communications-oriented functions. The functions, or specifications of the protocols concerned, will often stray into the so called upper layers (or processor-oriented functions). Particular emphasis is placed upon the data link and network control functions which are those responsible for the reliable transfer of data to the correct destination.

THE PHYSICAL LAYER

We begin our examination of specific classes of protocol by taking a brief look at the physical layer protocols. This chapter is not meant to provide a detailed examination of each of these protocols as selection of one in preference to another is seldom an option to the user. However, it applies the theory of the generalised approach to protocol examination, as discussed above, to a set of relatively simple protocols; and also illustrates the distinction between the physical interface itself and the protocols which operate across this interface.

Within a data communications system each DTE is connected to

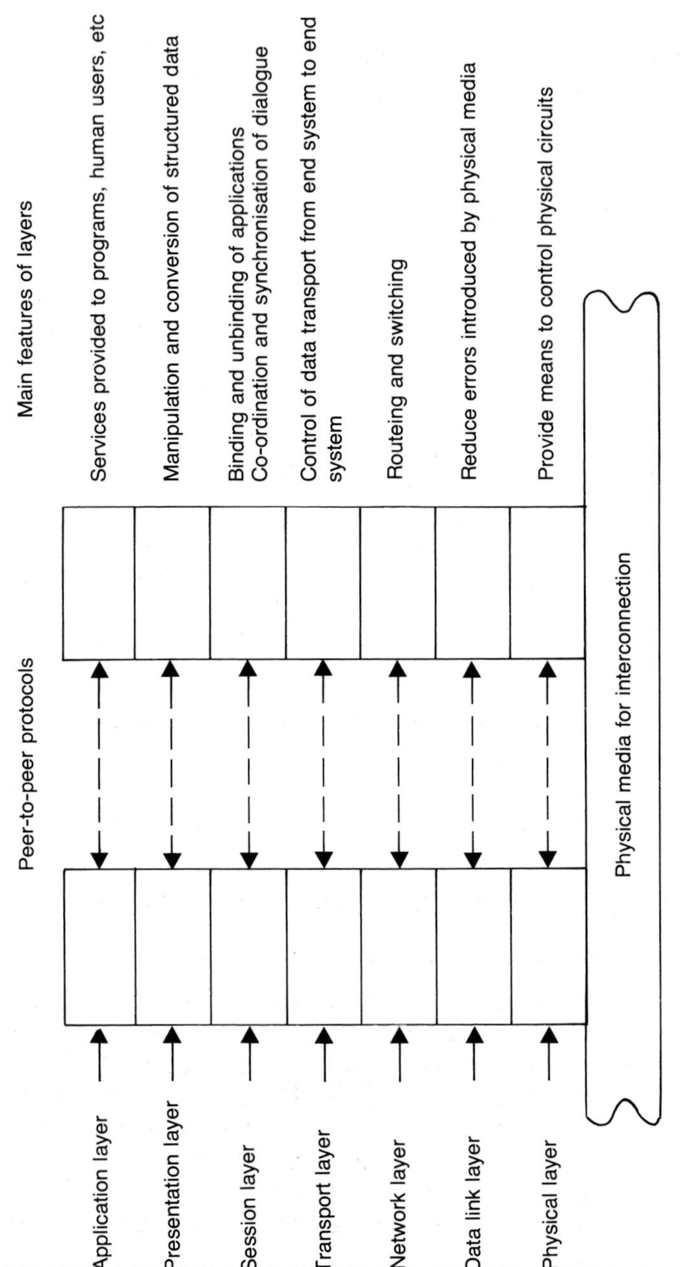

Figure 1.1 ISO Basic Reference Model for Open System Interconnection

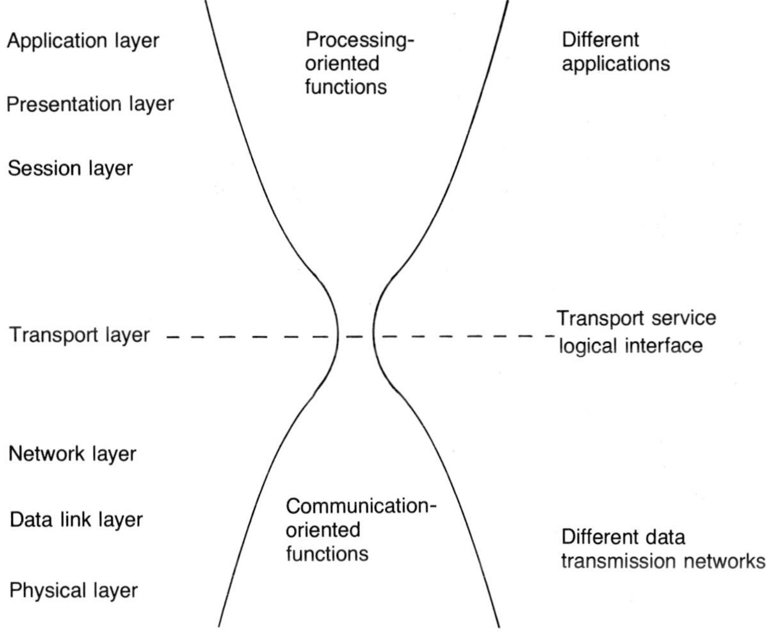

Figure 1.2 Upper and Lower Layers of ISO Model for OSI

the network via a physical interface. This interface may take many forms such as:

- — multi-pin connector ie 9, 15, 25 or 37 way D-type;
- — coaxial connector ie 50 or 75 ohm BNC.

Irrespective of the particular connector used in any instance, there is always a requirement for information to be transferred across this interface. The elements of this information which control or report on the behaviour of the DTE/DCE interface are governed by whichever physical layer protocol is being followed. Despite the differences in the physical characteristics of the various implementations of interface, the functional elements of all of them are broadly similar. These may be considered under the three elements listed above:

— syntax;

— semantics;

— behavioural sequence.

The syntax of physical layer protocols is given by the specification of the electrical characteristics of the interface connection. These characteristics include such elements as voltage levels, signal pulse shapes and electrical impedences. An important element of the syntax of the protocol is the synchronisation of signals. The two modes of synchronisation which are of particular interest here are those of *asynchronous* and *synchronous* operation. Note that it is important not to confuse the use of these two terms between the physical interface as described here and their use in the so called 'higher level' protocols which are described in the following chapters. At the physical level the difference is as follows:

— An interface signal which operates in asynchronous mode may alter its state at any moment in time, provided that the two successive changes do not occur within less than a specified time interval. For example an asynchronous signal operating over an interface rated at 1kHz may change state at any time, provided that at least 1msec has elapsed since the previous change in state;

— An interface signal which operates in synchronous mode may only change its state in phase with some other event. This event is usually a change in state of a timing signal which ensures a periodic structure for the information carried across the interface.

Under the CCITT V.24/V.28 synchronous interface specification*, each of the data signals operates in synchronisation with one

* Despite the proliferation of digital circuits and their associated X series recommendations, this remains as the dominant method of connection for data communications systems operating at data rates of below 20kbit/s. V.24 provides only a list of definitions for interchange circuits between a DTE and a DCE. It is not a full interface specification although many of the references to V.24 might suggest that it is. V.24 is usually implemented together with other recommendations for such characteristics as interface electrical characteristics (ie Rec V.28, V.10 or V.11) and pin allocation (ie ISO 2110).

of the timing (clock) signals. Data transitions (if appropriate) occur when the timing signal changes from OFF to ON and the data signal is sampled (read) when the corresponding timing signal changes from ON to OFF. Figure 1.3 illustrates this relationship.

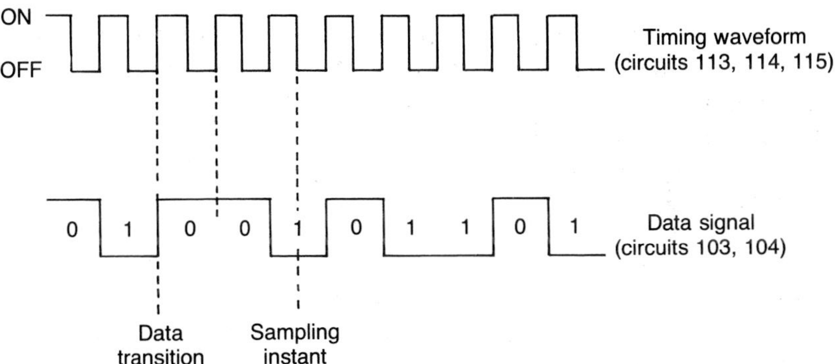

Figure 1.3 Relationship of Timing and Data Circuits for Synchronous Interface

The semantics of the protocol defines the meanings of the signals. Interfaces must convey three different types of information as listed below:

- data signals. These are the user data transmit (DCE to DTE) and receive (DCE to DTE) information signals;
- status (or supervisory) signals. These provide information concerning the ability of the DCE or DTE to provide or accept messages;
- control signals. These instruct the DCE or DTE to change operating mode.

There are three methods of achieving this:

- unifunctional interchange circuits. This method makes use of a number of pin connections, each of which carries only one type of information.
- signal controlled multifunctional circuits. This method has one interchange circuit for variable information (ie user data, DCE control). The type of information is defined by the state of one or more control circuits on the interface.

— message controlled multifunctional circuits. This method has only one interchange circuit for each direction of transmission (or possibly one circuit shared between both directions) and the context of the information being transferred across the interface is determined either by a header message at the beginning of each message, or by earlier messages which have set a particular context.

In a multi-pin connector arrangement the meaning of a signal may be determinable by the actual pin on which it appears. In a single pin system the meaning may be determined by a combination of the signal itself and the current and previous states of the interface.

The transfer of information by behavioural sequence is rarely used in physical-level protocols. This is due to the 'non intelligent' characteristics of the interface mechanisms themselves. Examples of behavioural sequence will however be met extensively in the remainder of this book.

The physical interface properties described above provide only sufficient facilities to allow strings of binary digits to be conveyed from DCE to DTE. Even assuming that the transmission network delivers this information to the recipient DTE the physical protocols provide no meaning or structure to these strings. These requirements are met by the Data Link level protocols.

2 Data Link Control Protocols

INTRODUCTION

It has been shown that data communications protocols span a range of functions and responsibilities. The next level that is considered here is that of the Data Link Control Protocols (DLCPs). These are particularly important for various reasons; for example:

- they are apparent in all data communications systems. The functions of the higher-level protocols, although always achieved by some means, are not always recognised and treated as part of the data communications system;
- designers, operators and users of systems often have a choice of the type of DLCP to be used. Indeed in many systems there will be several implementations which will commonly be used. A wise choice as to which particular option to select can only be made if the advantages and disadvantages of each of the various versions are understood.

DLCPs provide mechanisms for the end-to-end communications of information across data communications networks.

The end-to-end element of the requirement of the DLCP restricts its use to that of pre-established communications circuits. A pre-established circuit may consist of a dedicated circuit such as a leased telephone line or a switched circuit for which the circuit set-up phase has been completed. An example of the latter case is that of a PSTN circuit which is used in conjunction with modems. The act of establishing the end-to-end network connection consists of making the necessary telephone call and switching the telephone circuit from the handsets to the modems. This procedure is outside that of the DLCP and must be completed separately. Once this procedure has been completed the DLCP is then responsible for the session. Similarly, once the session is completed, the responsibility for resetting (or releasing) the telephone connections is outside that of the DLCP. Where this phase of the transmission system is automated the protocols used to control the network connection are the Network Layer protocols as described briefly in the previous chapter and in greater detail in Chapter 6.

The physical interfaces and protocols used are also outside the boundaries of concern of the DLCP. They are served by physical level interfaces and protocols such as those described in the previous chapter. Hence the DLCP does not need concern itself with the physical interface between the DTE and the DCE.

SETTING THE SCENE

Before examining the details of DLCPs it would be prudent to consider some of the characteristics of the networks over which they might have to operate.

Transmission Modes

The first of these characteristics is that of 'transmission mode'. The expression 'transmission mode' has differing meanings dependent upon the context in which it is used. When talking about data links it is used to describe the time relationships by which two or more devices may communicate. There are three modes of transmission, simplex, half duplex and full duplex.

Simplex means that there is only one direction of information flow. It is rather like a one-way street in that traffic flows in one direction only, but not necessarily continually. An example of a simplex transmission system is that of a single-keyboard and single-printer arrangement. Simplex transmission is illustrated in Figure 2.1.

Half-duplex operation means that information can flow in either direction but not at the same time. It is rather like a single track road. Traffic can flow in one direction, but this flow must cease before it travels in the opposite direction. A practical example is that of a two-wire baseband-modem link. Half-duplex operation is illustrated in Figure 2.2.

Full-duplex operation permits information to flow in both directions at the same time. In this case our analogy refers us to a two-lane road along which traffic can flow in both directions, independent of the traffic flowing in the opposite direction. In this case a practical example is given by a four-wire circuit modem, connecting a keyboard and printer set to a similar arrangement. Full-duplex operation is illustrated in Figure 2.3.

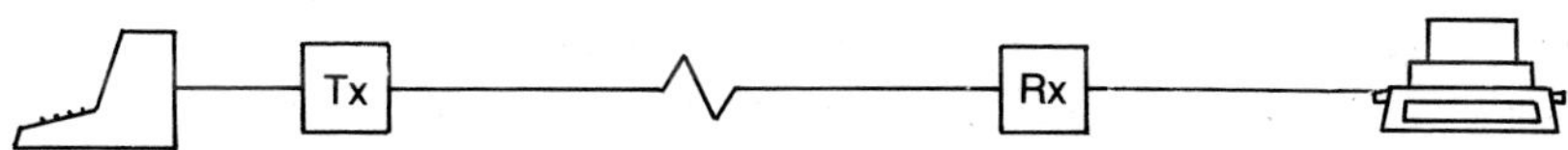

Figure 2.1 Simplex Transmission

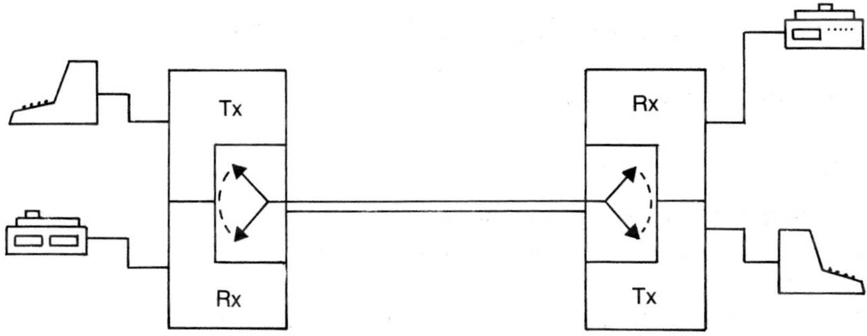

Figure 2.2 Half-Duplex Transmission

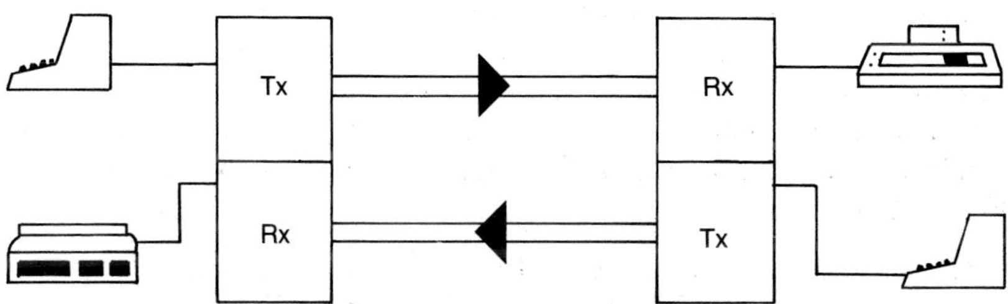

Figure 2.3 Full-Duplex Operation

When individual components, of differing mode capability, are connected to form a communications system the mode of the system becomes that of the lowest common denominator. For example, Figure 2.4 shows a terminal that can communicate in only simplex mode (a printer), with a transmission system and host system that are capable of operating in full-duplex mode. The resultant system operates in simplex mode.

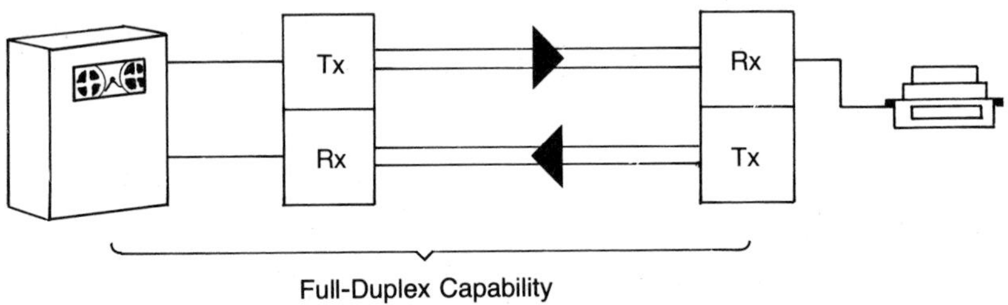

Figure 2.4 Simplex Operation over Full-Duplex Circuit

Another example is found when considering a DLCP that operates in half-duplex mode but is used across a communications circuit with full-duplex capability. The resultant communications will take place in half-duplex mode.

In the first example given above, the printer may be a single device within a terminal cluster, discussed below. The cluster itself may relay status information to the host system. In this case we might find a full-duplex transmission system (modem to modem) which carried a half-duplex DLC. Finally, the information to the printer would be in simplex mode. Figure 2.5 illustrates this nesting of transmission modes.

Network Topologies

We have stated that DLCs operate over pre-established communications circuits. There are many configurations of these circuits which may be constructed and these configurations will in turn play an important part in describing the requirements of the DLC. An analysis of network topologies shows three basic systems. These are Tree, Ring and Bus networks.

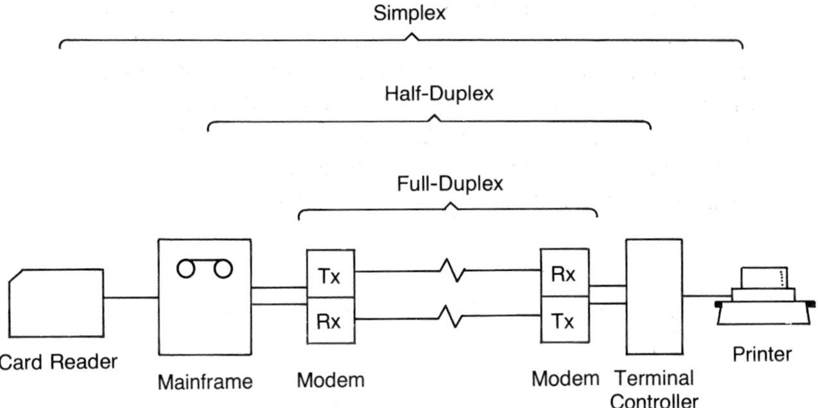

Figure 2.5 Nesting of Transmission Modes

Tree Networks:

A tree network consists of a single 'primary' (or master) node which may be regarded as the root of the tree and a number of 'secondary' (or slave) nodes which may be regarded as the leaves of the tree. The main characteristics of the system are as follows:

— whatever is transmitted by the primary is received by all of the secondaries. Hence if there is more than one secondary the primary must be able to indicate the intended recipient(s) of messages that it originates and each secondary must be able to determine whether received information is to be accepted or ignored. This demands that an addressing system is implemented;

— whatever is transmitted by any of the secondaries is received by only the primary;

— all secondaries share a common channel to the primary. Hence only one secondary may transmit to the primary at any instant. If more than one secondary attempts to transmit at any instant all secondary to primary transmissions at that instant will be corrupted. This demands that the DLC provides access control from secondary to primary.

A typical tree network is illustrated in Figure 2.6. It should be noted that the multi-level structure of the secondary nodes as shown in Figure 2.6 does not imply any special associations between nodes with common branches, such as nodes B and D or nodes C, E and F. Such diagrams may be drawn in many valid ways although they may reflect some secondary characteristic of the network such as the physical location of the nodes.

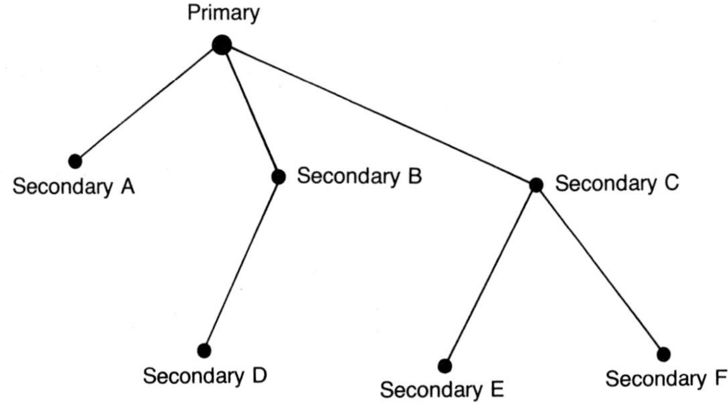

Figure 2.6 Tree Network

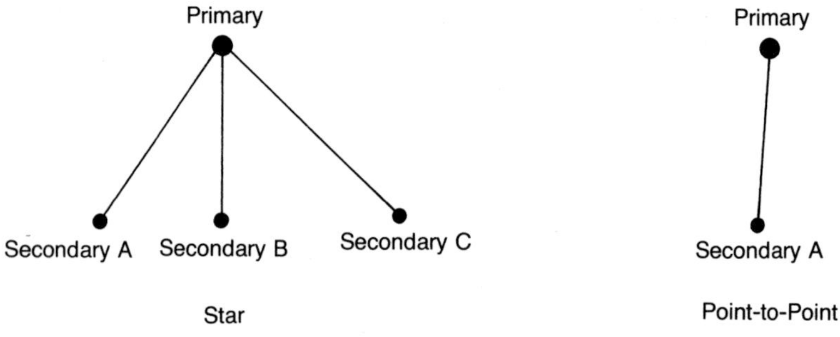

Figure 2.7 Star and Point-to-Point Networks

Two variations of tree networks are star networks and point-to-point circuits. A star network may be regarded as a tree network with only one level of secondary node and a point-to-point circuit may be regarded as a tree network with only one secondary node. In the case of the point-to-point circuit, some of the line access or secondary addressing requirements are redundant although they may still be implemented in the DLC. These topologies are illustrated in Figure 2.7.

Ring Networks:

Ring networks consist of a number of nodes which are connected in a ring formation as is illustrated in Figure 2.8. Each node receives messages from the previous node in the ring and must forward them to the next. This type of network has various characteristics:

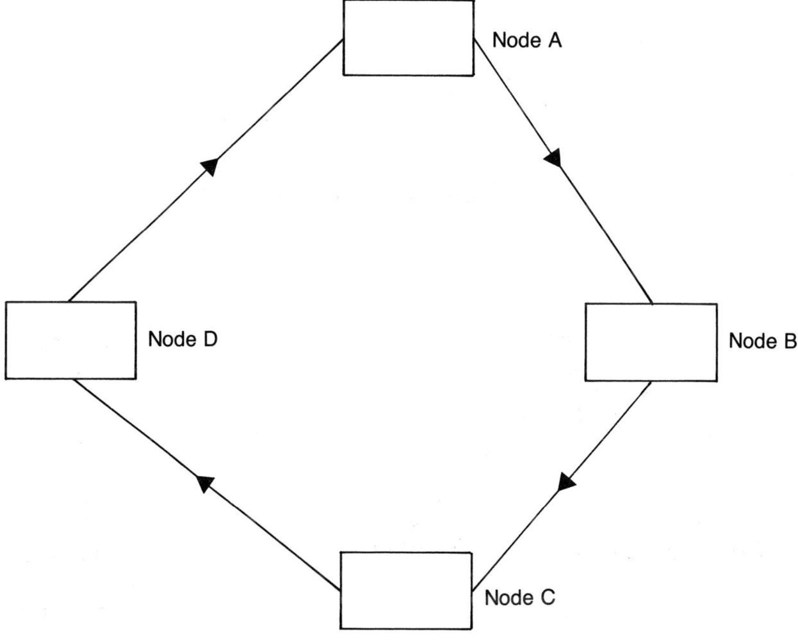

Figure 2.8 Ring Network

— any node may originate a message for any other node. This produces the requirement that the message must contain information to identify the intended recipient(s), ie an addressing system;

— messages will continue to circulate around the ring until they are removed. Hence a mechanism for achieving this must be provided.

Bus Networks:

In a 'Bus' topology network all transmitters and receivers are connected together. This is illustrated in Figure 2.9. The characteristics of bus networks are:

— whatever is transmitted by any node is received by all other nodes. Hence provision for a means of identifying the intended recipient(s) of a message must be made, ie addressing.

— if more than one node attempts to transmit at any instant, both messages will be corrupted. This demands that some form of line access mechanism is implemented.

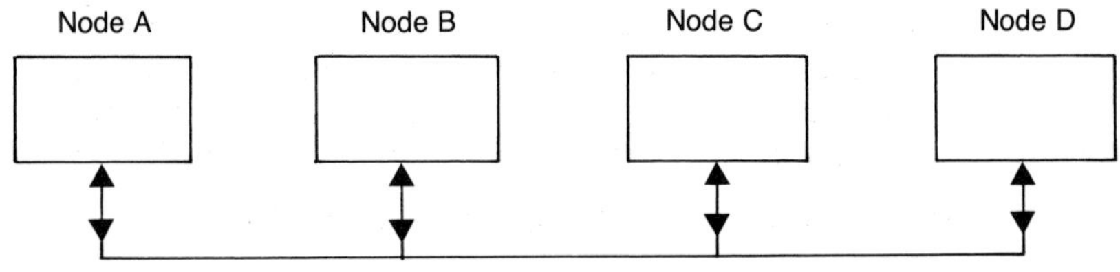

Figure 2.9 Bus Network

ERROR CONTROL

Transmission networks are subject to errors. Put simply, the information delivered by the network to the output nodes is not necessarily a true reflection of that entered into the network at the input nodes. It is therefore desirable to build into a communications system, some form of error control. This is one of the DLC functions, although other types of error control may be used additionally. In fact there are no systems which will detect and/or correct every possible error. It is only possible to minimise the possibility of incorrect information being accepted.

There are two aspects of error control:

— *error detection* is the process of determining whether an error has occurred or not;

— *error correction* is the process by which the correct information is determined once an error has been detected.

Error Detection

There are two techniques which are commonly used in data transmission systems:

— information feedback systems;

— parity error detection.

Each of these is discussed in more detail in the following sections.

Terminals and Hosts

Having identified the various network topologies over which the data systems may communicate it is now time to consider the structure of the data systems themselves. For the purpose of simplicity, it is possible to consider only two types of device, namely, a terminal system (terminal) and the host computer system (host).

A terminal system has the following characteristics:

— it may consist of a number of component devices, ie VDUs, printers, storage devices, etc. Each of these is connected to a common cluster controller. It is the cluster controller which communicates with the distant device. This is illustrated in Figure 2.10;

— each cluster controller may maintain only one communication session with a distant device. Hence all devices on a single terminal system may only communicate with the same distant system during any session;

— within the distant system each of the terminal system

devices may hold a communications session with different applications or devices.

This is illustrated in Figure 2.11.

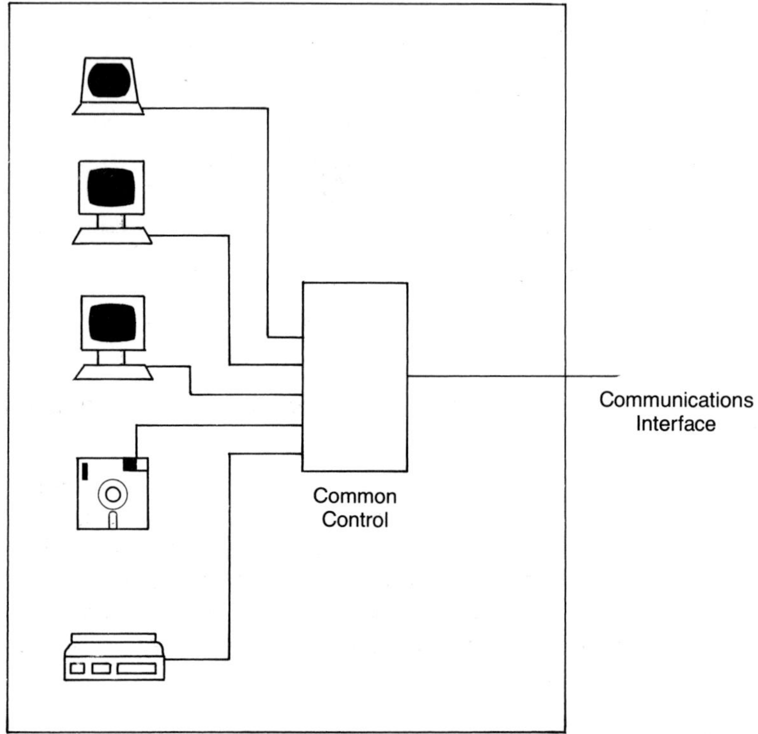

Figure 2.10 Clustered Terminal System

A host computer system has the following characteristics:

— it consists of a number of component devices and a number of applications systems. Each of these is connected to the communications system via a single front end processor (FEP);

— an FEP may communicate concurrently with many external devices. An FEP has many communications ports (physical interfaces), each of which may be communicating with many external systems (either terminals or other hosts).

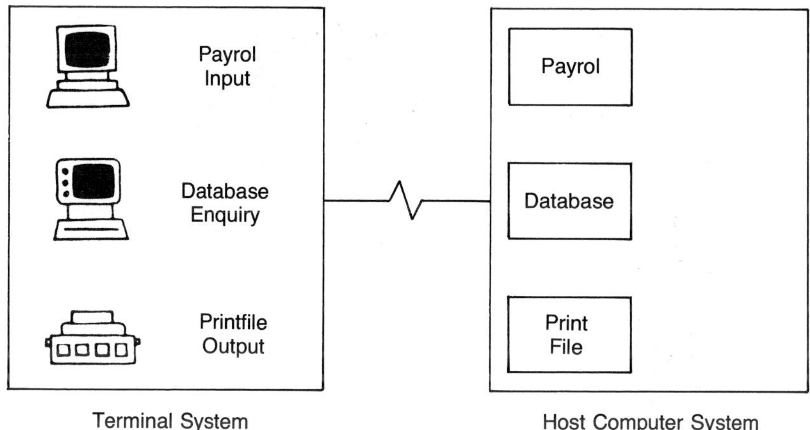

Figure 2.11 Terminal to Host Mapping

A typical host to terminals communications system is illustrated in Figure 2.12.

It should not be forgotten that a host system may communicate directly with another host system and likewise a terminal system may communicate directly with another terminal system. This does not invalidate the approach taken here as in such cases one of the devices may be considered to be a host system and the other a terminal. Indeed this is the approach taken by many of the designers and implementors of such systems.

FRAMING

A further consideration to be made is that of the units of information which must be transferred across the network. The purpose of a DLCP is to provide a mechanism to transfer an unspecified quantity of information from a source to one or more sinks. It is convenient (and also valid) to consider this information to be finite. We shall consider this information in its entirety to be a file. It may not be convenient to transfer an entire file in a single operation and so the file may be segmented into more manageable units. We shall call these units transmission blocks or frames. Finally, it may be convenient to construct each transmission block from individual characters or data bytes.

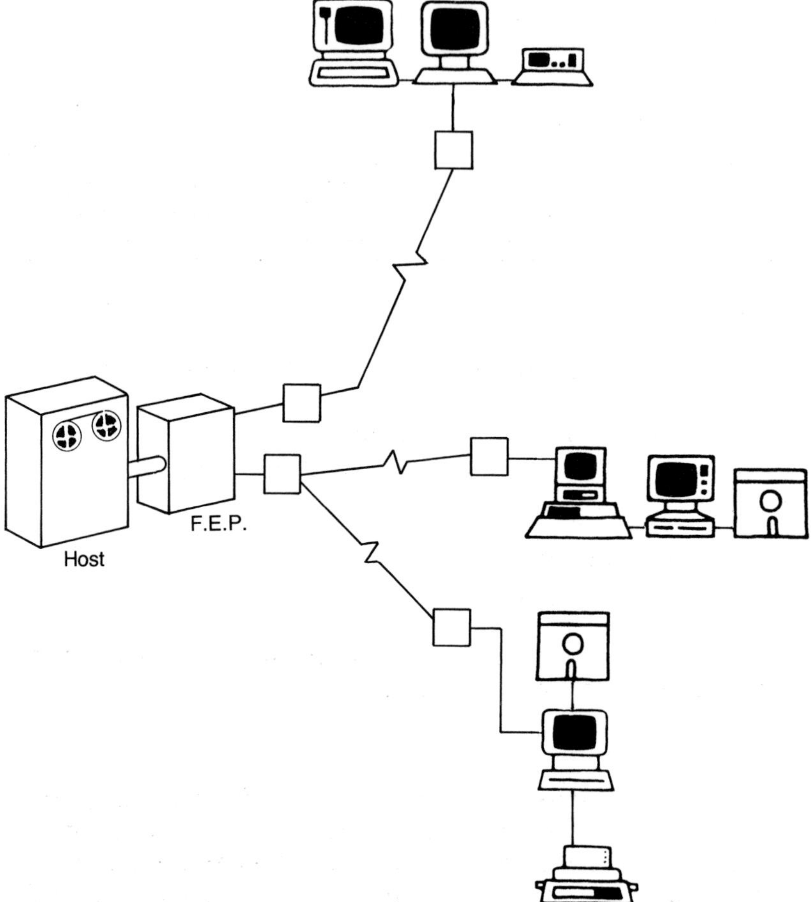

Figure 2.12 Host and Terminals Communications Network

Hence the three units of information are:

— files;

— blocks;

— characters.

Figure 2.13 illustrates this structuring of information. Each of these elements may be transferred between DTEs in a nested

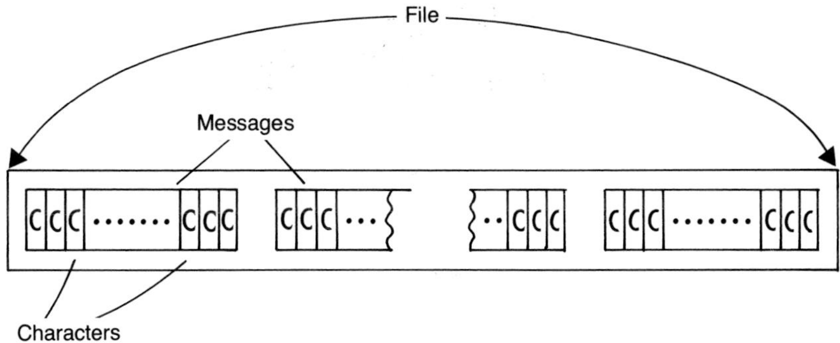

Figure 2.13 Nested Structure of Information

manner. The transmission at each level may be regarded as a communications session and it is therefore necessary to:

— initiate the session;

— transfer information;

— terminate the session.

The process of session initiation and termination at the character and block level is known as framing.

FLOW CONTROL

Consider a data processing system in which a file on a magnetic tape is read on a mainframe computer system. The information in the file is then transmitted to a terminal system and output on a printer. Assume that the size of the file is unspecified and the printing must begin as soon as possible (certainly before the entire file is read from the tape). The basic method of transferring this information is to read the unit of information from the tape, transmit the information to the remote terminal and then print it on the output device. The various activities may be listed more precisely as follows:

— read blocks (of size a) of information from the tape;

— assemble transmission blocks (of size b) consisting of information from the tape plus transmission control information;

— transmit these blocks to the remote terminal cluster;

— remove the required information from the transmission blocks;

— assemble print blocks (size c);

— print the information.

This procedure is illustrated in Figure 2.14. There are two important points which may be seen in this diagram. The first is that the various information blocks may be of different sizes. The second is that the speed of information movement say from the tape to the tape buffer, across the transmission network or from the print buffer to the printer may be at different rates. Hence provision must be made such that information may arrive at an element in the system at an instantaneous rate which is greater than that at which it leaves that element. For instance the instantaneous rate at which the information reaches the print buffer might be 100 cps (characters per second) but the printer may operate at only 30 cps. This places two demands throughout the system:

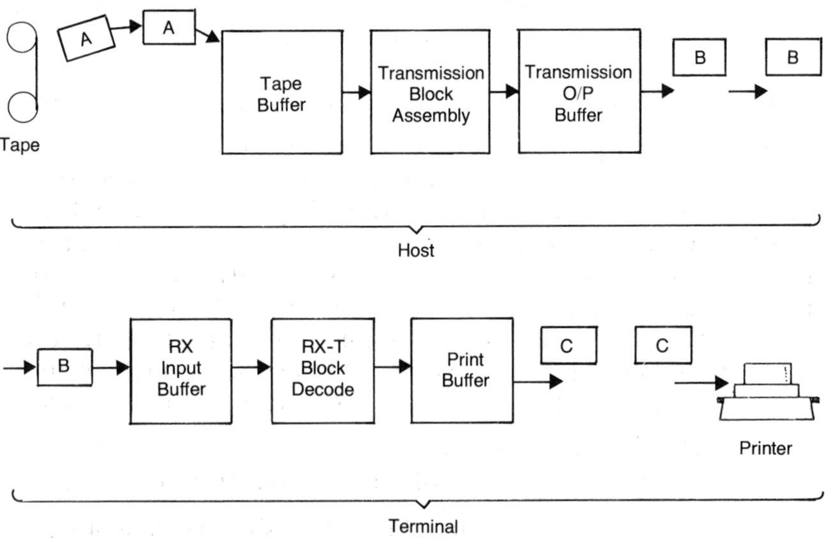

Figure 2.14 Information Flow

- — a means of buffering information is required. This may only be of small capacity but a minimum requirement is that it should be able to accommodate one complete information block;
- — if the buffer is liable to become full or even to overflow it is necessary to halt temporarily the flow of information. This is known as flow control.

Buffering

One of the requirements for the provision of buffering facilities was outlined in the previous section. There are in fact many requirements for the provision of buffers, some of which are mandatory in that without them communications would be impossible, and the others which are optional in that they serve to improve the speed at which end-to-end communications takes place. In the latter case they may be omitted in order to reduce the cost of implementing the communications system. The main requirements for buffering are:

- — to enable speed conversion to take place between different elements of the communications system;
- — to allow blocks of information to have different sizes throughout the system;
- — to provide temporary storage of information blocks whilst error handling and other supervisory functions are carried out.

The requirements listed above all fall into the mandatory category, but what about the optional buffering facilities? Consider the case of a terminal system which is receiving data which is being output on a printer. The basic routine is as follows:

1) Receive the transmission block into receive buffer.
2) Validate transmission block (error control, etc).
3) Print the required information.
4) Signal to the source that a further block may be sent.

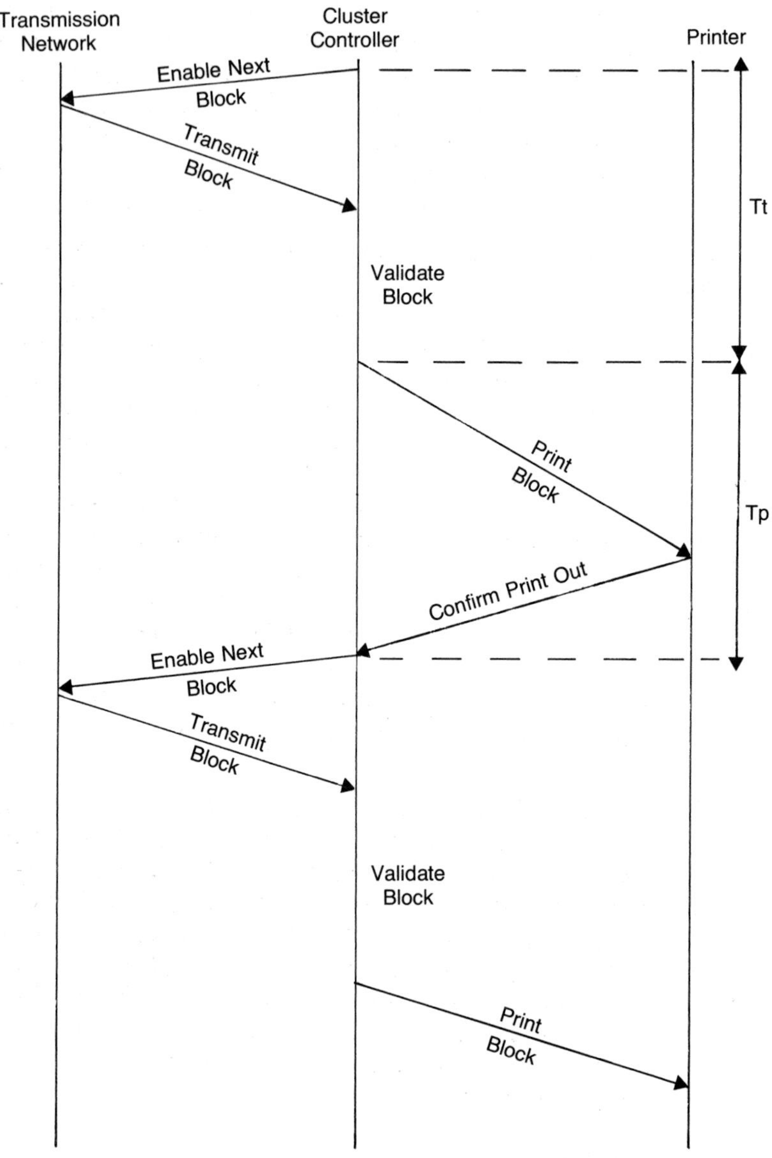

Figure 2.15 Single Buffer Transmission and Print

This is a feasible scenario which is in practice implemented in many systems. The inefficiency in this system is associated with stage 3). Having transferred one information block in stage 1) and validated it in stage 2) the transmission system remains idle during stage 3). This is illustrated in Figure 2.15. This system is said to be single buffered and the time taken to transfer each block of information through this section of the system equals Tt + Tp.

Now consider the case where the terminal system has two buffers: one which receives data from the network and holds it during verification and the second which holds the print information during printing. This may be two buffers each allocated the specific purpose described above, or two similar buffers which toggle between receiving data and printing it. Figure 2.16 illustrates the second case in which buffers A and B alternate between the printing and receiving functions. When examining this diagram note that neither the transmission network nor the printer need be aware that two buffers are being used. It can be seen from the diagram that the printer is now operating continuously and the time taken to transfer each block of information through this section of the system is the greater of Tt and Tp (in our example this is Tp). Hence if Tp = Tt a saving of 50% is achieved. If we extend the use of multiple buffering to the transmitting device, even greater improvement in the overall system efficiency is achieved.

Although it can be argued that this form of buffering is outside the responsibility of a protocol it serves to illustrate that one protocol might perform very much differently within two different environments. In many cases both systems described above are supported by one protocol but it has been shown that performance in terms of throughput can vary by a factor as high as three-to-one. We shall also see that some protocols provide buffering facilities which are very similar to those described above and can improve throughput by even greater factors, as compared with some other protocol implementations.

TRANSMISSION CODES

During the transfer of information from a source to a sink that information may be represented in many different physical forms.

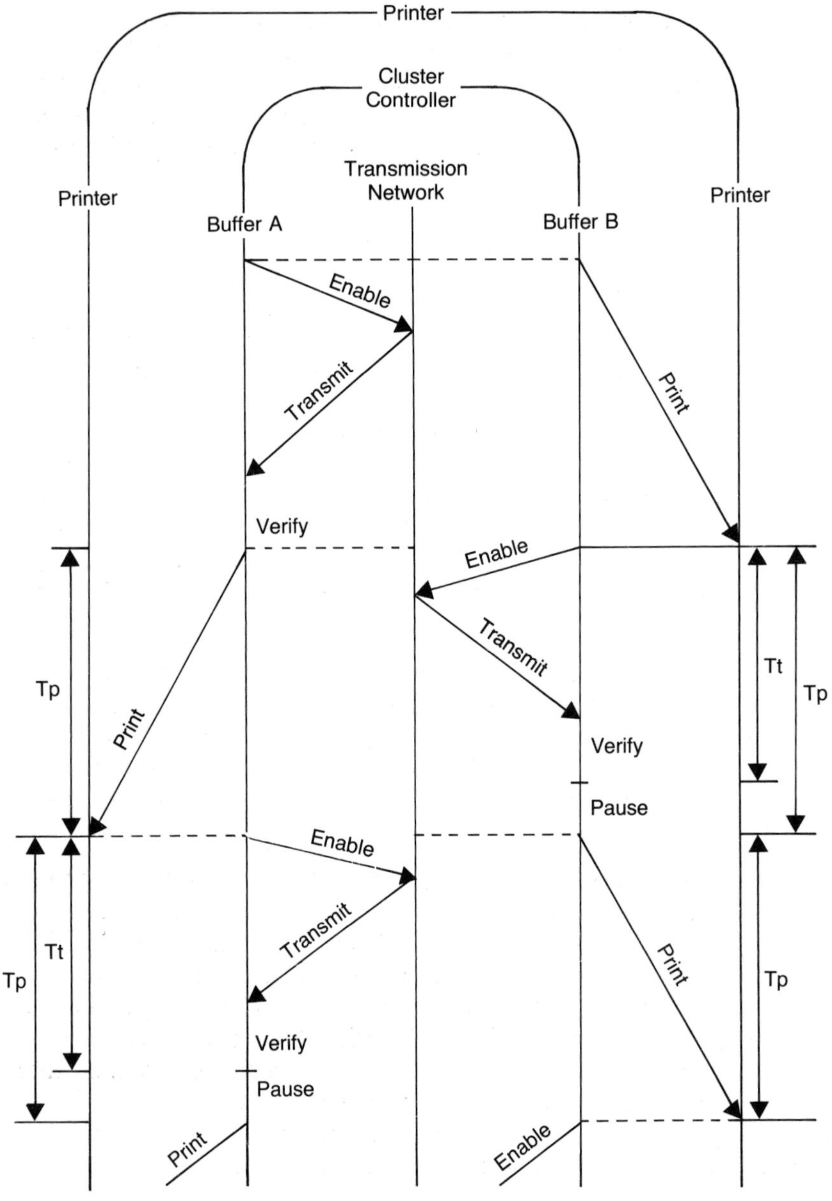

Figure 2.16 Double Buffered Transmission and Print

These include magnetic image, electrical voltages, currents or fields, electromagnetic waves, optical signals, etc. Similarly the information may be represented in many logical or abstract forms. Consider the case of the alphabetic character 'H'. This may be represented in the following three ways (as well as many others):

— 10100 (Baudot)

— 11001000 (EBCDIC)

— 1001000 (ASCII)

It is essential that the implementation of a DLCP at all nodes in a network is aligned with the form of the information which is being transmitted. Some DLCPs only operate under one transmission code in which case it is essential that a prospective user is aware of any restrictions which this might create. Some DLCPs do not send the information as characters but merely transmit it as a string of bits (see Chapter 5). Even in this situation there are certain patterns of these strings which have special meanings and a parallel can be drawn between these and the traditional, 'byte oriented' transmission systems.

As is indicated above there are a number of different code sets which have been developed to answer various requirements or conditions without replacing existing sets. The two most commonly used transmission code sets are ASCII and EBCDIC and these will be described in some detail below. Other codes include the Baudot code used for telex.

The ancestry of the EBCDIC (Extended Binary Coded Decimal Interchange Code) code can be traced through its name. The Adam or Eve of EBCDIC was the Binary Coded Decimal code. This was developed to provide a code which was suitable for computer applications (hence the binary element) but could be easily used by people (hence the decimal element). This code was then developed to cater for alphabetic and symbol characters forming the 6-bit Binary Coded Decimal Interchange Code (BCDIC). At this stage differing interpretations were made for certain characters to allow for commercial or scientific usage.

The next generation was the Extended Binary Coded Decimal code which added a parity bit to the six-data bit code of BCDIC

B I T S			4	0	0	0	0	0	0	0	0	1	1	1	1	1	1	1	1
			3	0	0	0	0	1	1	1	1	0	0	0	0	1	1	1	1
			2	0	0	1	1	0	0	1	1	0	0	1	1	0	0	1	1
			1	0	1	0	1	0	1	0	1	0	1	0	1	0	1	0	1
8	7	6	5																
0	0	0	0	NUL				PF	HT	LC	DEL								
0	0	0	1					RES	NL	BS	IL								
0	0	1	0					BYP	LF	EOB	PRE			SM					
0	0	1	1					PN	RS	UC	EOT								
0	1	0	0	SP										¢	.	<	(	+	|
0	1	0	1	&										!	$	*	)	;	¬
0	1	1	0	-	/									^	,	%	—	>	?
0	1	1	1											:	#	@	'	=	"
1	0	0	0		a	b	c	d	e	f	g	h	i						
1	0	0	1		j	k	l	m	n	o	p	q	r						
1	0	1	0			s	t	u	v	w	x	y	z						
1	0	1	1																
1	1	0	0		A	B	C	D	E	F	G	H	I						
1	1	0	1		J	K	L	M	N	O	P	Q	R						
1	1	1	0			S	T	U	V	W	X	Y	Z						
1	1	1	1	0	1	2	3	4	5	6	7	8	9						

Figure 2.17 EBCDIC Code Set

and also provided upper- and lower-case capabilities. This code also provided certain machine and transmission control characters such as tabulation characters and transmission block control characters. The last descendent (for the present at least) is the Extended Binary Coded Decimal Interchange Code (EBCDIC). This is an 8 data bit code and hence has the capacity of 256 separate characters. This provides for both upper- and lower-case alphabetic characters without the need to use shift sequences and various control characters. There are several unallocated charac-

B I T S			3	0	0	0	0	1	1	1
			2	0	0	1	1	0	0	1
			1	0	1	0	1	0	1	0
8	7	6	5							
C	0	0	NUL	DLE	SP	0	@	P		p
0	0	0	SOH	DC1	!	1	A	Q	a	q
0	0	1	STX	DC2	"	2	B	R	b	r
0	0	1	ETX	DC3	#	3	C	S	c	s
0	1	0	EOT	DC4	$	4	D	T	d	t
0	1	0	ENQ	NAK	%	5	E	U	e	u
0	1	1	ACK	SYN	&	6	F	V	f	v
0	1	1	BEL	ETB	'	7	G	W	g	w
1	0	0	BS	CAN	(	8	H	X	h	x
1	0	0	HT	EM	)	9	I	Y	i	y
1	0	1	LF	SUB	*	:	J	Z	j	z
1	0	1	VT	ESC	+	;	K	[	k	{
1	1	0	FF	FS	,	<	L	\	l	|
1	1	0	CR	FS	–	=	M	]	m	}
1	1	1	SO	RS	.	>	N	^	n	~
1	1	1	SI	US	/	?	O	—	o	DEL

Figure 2.18 ASCII Code Set

ters which can be assigned on a local basis. Figure 2.17 provides details of the EDCDIC code.

The ASCII (American National Standard Code for Information Interchange) code is used for more data transmission systems than any other code. It is a 7 data bit code containing both machine and communications control characters as well as the transmitted information characters. Figure 2.18 provides details of the ASCII 2-code set.

In practice variations of these code sets (either standardised or customised) may be found in some applications such as scientific work where special characters are required.

EMULATION

Having designed protocols (both at DLCP and higher level) to achieve information transfer between specific devices (say a card reader and a printer) it is useful if the same protocols can be used to achieve communications between other devices (say a terminal and a magnetic tape device). One method of doing this is to make the terminal act as if it were a card reader and produce input messages in card image. Similarly, the magnetic tape device may be made to act like a printer – this is known as emulation and the software which achieves this is known as an emulator. In a similar vein a device produced by one supplier may be made to act as if it were a device produced by a different supplier, this is another form of emulation.

SUMMARY

This chapter has taken a 'Cooks' tour through the world of DLCPs. In doing so, attention has been drawn to many of the requirements of a DLCP. The following list provides a summary of the features of DLCPs derived from both requirements and solutions as listed in this chapter. DLCPs must therefore provide:

— a means of establishing a communications session across a pre-established communications network;

— a means of transferring information reliably during that session;

— a means of terminating the session.

In order to achieve this specific requirements are for:

— an addressing system;

— a network access system;

— an error control system;

— framing mechanisms;

— flow control mechanisms;

— common transmission code.

CLASSIFYING DLCPs

Most of the remainder of this book is devoted to providing an explanation of the operation of DLCPs. In order to structure this information into an easily understood form it is useful to identify types of DLCP and to investigate the characteristics of each type in turn. The most common method of classifying DLCPs provides us with the following groups:

— asynchronous TTY DLCPs;

— synchronous byte mode DLCPs;

— synchronous bit mode DLCPs.

The following chapters will analyse the characteristics of each of these groups in turn. As with most systems of classification, there are some DLCPs which will fit into more than one of the above groups (there may well be some DLCPs that do not fit into any of the groups but they are not known to the author). The general characteristics of each group may be summarised:

Asynchronous DLCPs	–	Point to point operation Transmission of characters (or bytes) Error detection is by VRC No error correction
Synchronous Byte Mode DLCPs (also known as Basic	–	Transmission of characters (or bytes) Error detection is by LRC/VRC Error correction is by stop and wait

Mode DLCPs)		repeated transmission Transmission is in half-duplex mode
Synchronous Bit-Oriented DLCPs (also known as High-Level DLCPs)	–	Transmission is bit oriented Error detection is by CRC Error correction is by 'go back n' or 'selective repeat' re-transmission Transmission is in full-duplex mode

The characteristics listed above may not mean too much to the reader but the following sections will explain each of them in turn. The book now proceeds by investigating the first of these classes: that of asynchronous TTY DLCPs.

3 Asynchronous DLCPs

INTRODUCTION

There are two families of asynchronous DLCP. These are the 'Teletype (TTY) Emulators' and the more advanced 'ACK/NACK' systems. The ACK/NACK protocols act in very much the same manner as the byte mode synchronous DLCPs which are described in detail in Chapter 4 and as such this chapter concentrates on the more common TTY emulator family. There are certain areas (eg character framing) which are common to both families and as such the reader is advised to ensure his understanding of the material in this chapter before progressing to the more advanced protocols to follow. For completeness a brief introduction to ACK/NACK working is given towards the end of this chapter.

Use of asynchronous transmission techniques in data communications was, until recently, in danger of being swamped by the proliferation of faster, more reliable (in terms of error handling) and more versatile synchronous-based systems. However, asynchronous systems are enjoying something of a comeback in the marketplace. One of the main reasons for this revival is the introduction of 'personal' and 'home' computers. These may require communications which will have the following characteristics:

— occasional use. The requirement for communications may not be frequent but may still be mandatory;

— they may be used for interactive access to information databases or for data file or program file transfer;

— compatibility is essential. Communications with a wide variety of systems, often non-manufacturer specific, are required. The range of systems with which compatibility is required is often unknown at the time of equipment selection (this applies to both hardware and software);

— low-cost systems are required both in terms of initial outlay such as hardware or software purchase and operating costs.

CHARACTERISTICS OF ASYNCHRONOUS TERMINALS

They will normally consist of a single input and a single output device. This can be viewed as a printer and a keyboard although storage devices such as disk units may be made to emulate these. More complex devices may use asynchronous transmission but the principles of operation of the DLCP are then more closely aligned with those of the synchronous byte mode DLCP, as described in Chapter 4.

The asynchronous terminals considered here are the 'grandchildren' of the electromechanical teletype (TTY) devices originally used for local communications from an operator to a computer system. The modern versions offer such improvements as fast operation, larger character set and more control functions, but essentially operate in the same manner. Versions of these devices in which a visual display replaces a printer are known as 'glass teletypes'.

FRAMING

Character Framing

In an asynchronous system (also known as 'stop/start' transmission), individual characters are transmitted without reference to previous or following characters. It is therefore necessary to provide a means by which the receiver can identify the beginning of each character. It is also desirable to confirm that a character has been completely received and that it has not been merged with a following character or some other form of interference. Hence it is desirable to indicate the end of a character. This framing is achieved by means of the start and stop bits of each character as is illustrated in Figure 3.1.

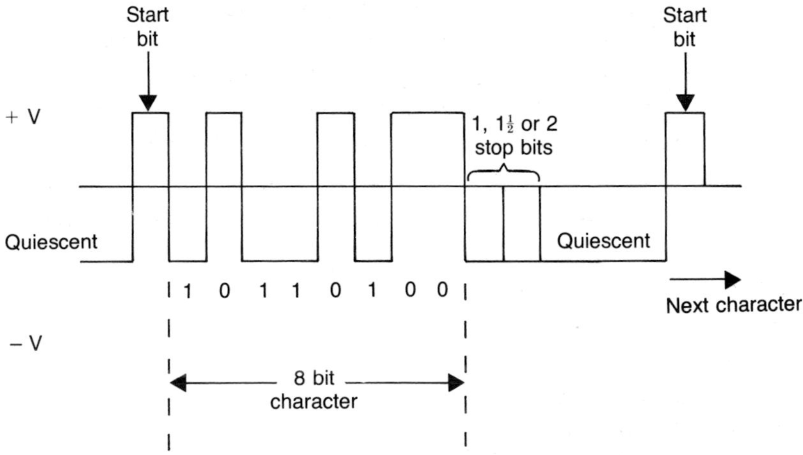

Figure 3.1 Asynchronous Character Framing

On initial inspection this would appear to present no problems. The difficulty arises because the number of stop bits is not consistent throughout all terminal systems. Although most systems operate with only one start bit it is common to use either one, one and a half or two stop bits. The method of selecting the number of stop bits varies from terminal to terminal but may be as follows:

— permanently fixed or only changeable by an engineering modification;

— selectable by switch (either hardware or software) within the terminal or, if the terminal is a computer in its own right, its operating system;

— dependent upon the communications software package which is being used (again applies to a computer-based terminal).

The second and third methods listed above illustrate that despite not being part of the DLCP in the strictest terms, this is certainly an aspect of the data link procedure that must be considered carefully.

One of the disadvantages of asynchronous transmission systems is that in terms of line utilisation they are rather inefficient. If a character has one start bit, one stop bit and eight data bits the framing information takes 20% of the utilised line time. This is quite satisfactory for slow-speed or low-volume transmissions where efficient line utilisation is not particularly important, but for high-speed or large-volume transmission it is desirable to increase the efficiency of operation.

Synchronous DLCPs offer much improved efficiency and are discussed in detail in Chapters 4 and 5.

Block Framing

More often referred to as a character mode protocol the asynchronous DLCPs often operate in 'block' mode, in this case the message block being a line of text. Consider a TTY connected to a host computer on an interactive basis. The operator inputs a line of text terminating it with a CR, hence the block framing is as follows:

— end of block is identified by CR;

— start of block is identified by first character input after CR.

The application system then processes this line of text as follows:

— verifies whether it is valid or not;

— determines the response;

— transmits the response.

In the system described above, the block framing is not part of the DLCP but is part of the application or communications handling system at the host end and is part of the operating procedure at the terminal end.

This technique has, however, been adopted by some DLCPs for automated file transfer. If a file is to be transferred from source to sink an asynchronous DLCP may be used which emulates this TTY procedure. More will be said about automatic TTY DLCPs towards the end of this chapter.

File Delimiters

There are of course two positions in a file which may require delimiting: these are the beginning and the end. The beginning of a file is usually indicated by sequence. This means that it is taken to be the first data to be received after an event, such as a command message.

Consider the case when inputting a file into a system. There will be some preamble with the system when the file name, etc is exchanged. Having completed this, the system will then invite the user to begin transmission, the next data input will be taken as the start of file. This implicit framing routine is common to many protocols. The end of file can be identified by a control character, this may be the EOT (end of transmission) character or be special to the application. As in the case of the block framing described above, this delimiting generally takes place outside the DLCP. Again, however, there are asynchronous DLCPs which emulate the human operator/system interaction and in these cases this function is part of the DLCP.

LINE ACCESS

Asynchronous DLCPs operate generally in point-to-point mode only. A special case of a point to multipoint example is given in Chapter 4 (Block Mode DLCPs). Thus, the only requirement for line access would be for use on half-duplex transmission network services. As we shall see in the section on error control, the majority of asynchronous systems require full-duplex transmission services and hence, will not have any line access control facilities.

ERROR CONTROL

Error Detection

There are two forms of error detection which may be used. These are:

— information feedback systems;

— parity error detection.

Information feedback systems are restricted to asynchronous systems and use a form of negative feedback. They operate as follows:

— any information input at a node is transmitted to its destination and then retransmitted back to the origin. The originating node then compares this information (which has been transmitted to and from the destination) with the original information to determine whether any errors have been induced.

The simplest form of this technique is that used for slow speed asynchronous TTY operation. Figure 3.2 shows the system in which a teletype is connected to a mainframe system. As the data is entered at the teletype it is transmitted to the mainframe without being displayed locally at the input. The recipient then loops back all received information to the source where it is displayed on the printer. The printed information may then be compared with the input information to detect whether any errors have occurred. This technique is often referred to as 'echoplexing'. NOTE: The error detection is performed by the operator and is therefore outside the DLCP. It is however convenient to consider this technique at this point so that it may be compared with the DLCP procedures which follow.

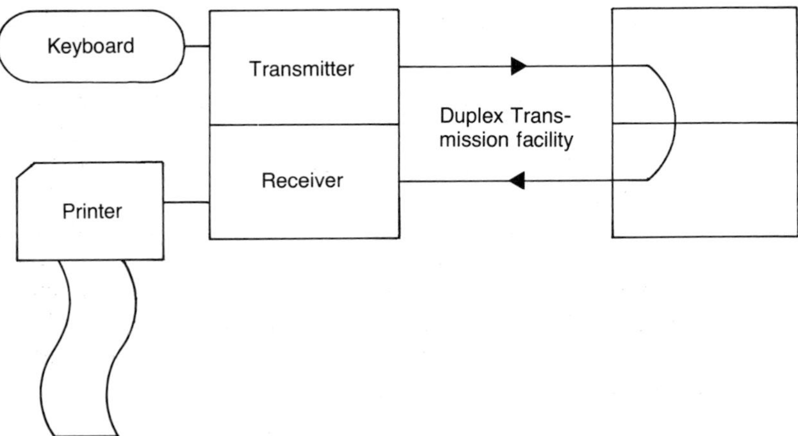

Figure 3.2 Information Feedback

The main problem with this system is that it detects errors in only one direction (from terminal to host). There is no error detection facility for information originated at the host and transmitted to the terminal. Other disadvantages with this system are as follows:

— it will 'detect' any errors which occur on the return path for information which originated from the terminal. Hence the apparent error rate will be twice that which is experienced;

— although only suitable for half-duplex information flow the system requires full-duplex transmission facilities.

Parity error detection works by performing some algorithm on the data to be transmitted to form a 'data value' dependent parity check. This parity check information is then transmitted in addition to the data, the recipient then performs the same algorithm on the received data and calculates the parity check value of the received data. This is compared with the parity check value received and if they are the same it is assumed that no errors have occurred. If the received and calculated parity checks do not agree then an error has occurred and an error recovery procedure must be initiated.

There are three types of parity error detection: Vertical Redundancy Checking (VRC); Lateral (or Longitudinal) Redundancy Checking (LRC); and Cyclic Redundancy Checking (CRC). Only VRC is used for asynchronous TTY operation. LRC and CRC are described in Chapters 4 and 5 respectively.

Vertical Redundancy Checking can be specified to operate as either an 'odd' parity system or 'even' parity system. In an odd parity system each unit of data (usually a character or byte) is examined in turn and the number of 'one' bits is determined. An additional bit (either a one bit or a zero bit) is added to each individual character such that the total of 'one' bits is then odd. This gives an odd parity to the character. If even parity is specified then the additional bit is added such that the total number of 'one' bits in the character is even. An example of odd parity detection is given in Figure 3.3.

The main advantage of VRC is that it is simple to implement, it is suitable for character-oriented protocols as error checking may be performed after each character has been received. It is also easy to implement this part of the terminal's hardware or, in the more modern case, firmware. The main disadvantage of VRC is that it is not particularly resilient. If two bits in a single character are incorrectly received, no error will be detected. Consider the example given above. Figure 3.4 illustrates the failure in this system if two bit errors occur.

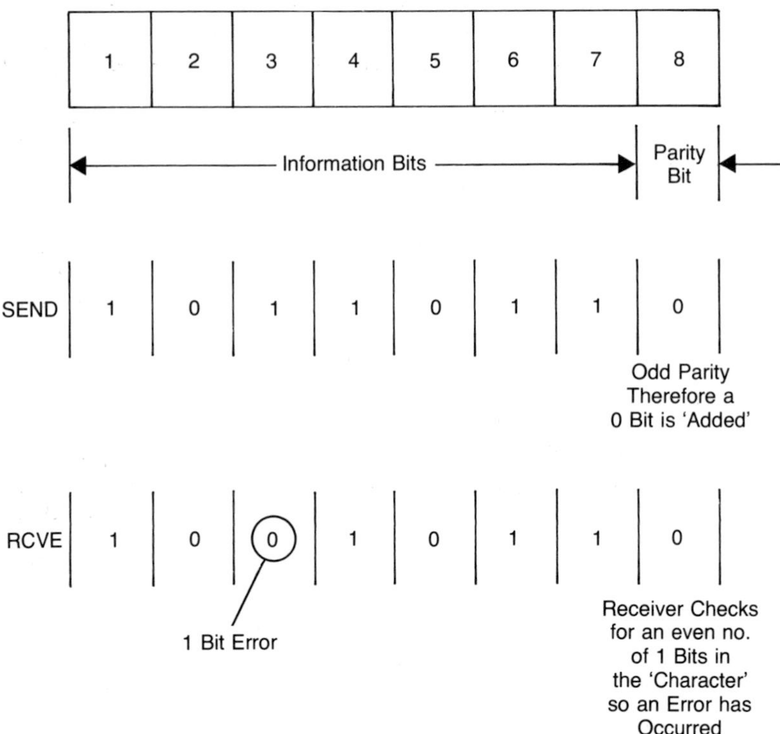

Figure 3.3 Character Parity Checking

Error Correction

A second aspect of error control is that of error correction. The 'simple' asynchronous DLCPs being discussed here offer no error correction facilities. It is the responsibility of the higher-level protocols to perform this function. In this case, however, the 'higher-level protocols' are usually performed by a human operator. As such they are not normally recognised as being part of the protocol. Despite their apparent misplacement it is convenient to consider these procedures at this point. There are three methods of dealing with erroneous messages:

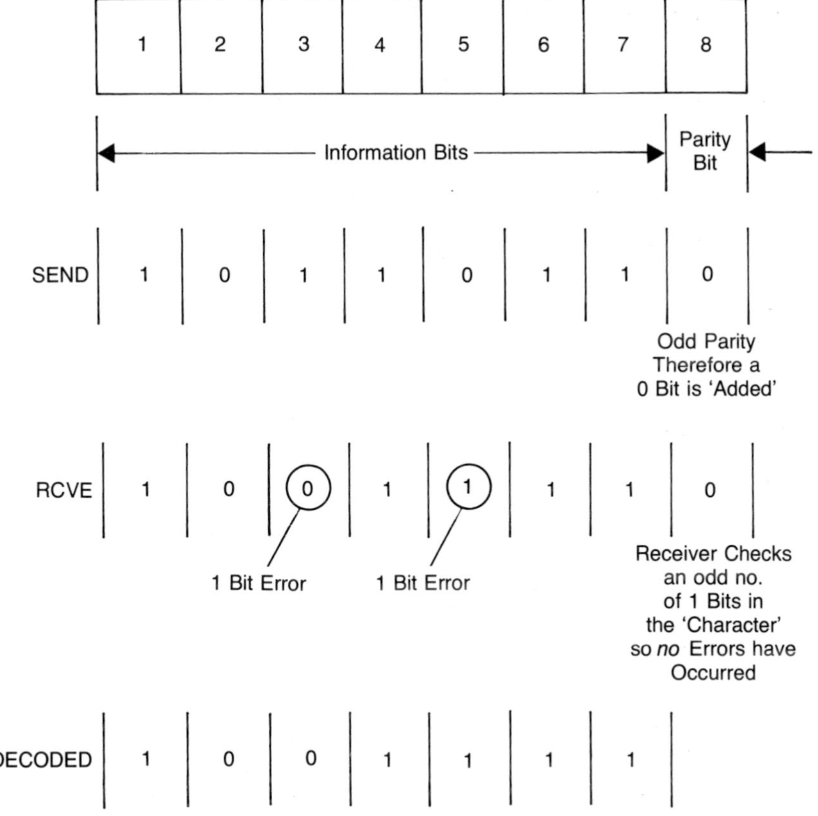

Figure 3.4 Character Parity Error Failure

— ignore them;

— repeat them;

— predict the correct content.

Each of these techniques is discussed below.

Ignoring errors is a thought that brings palpitations to the heart of the dp manager. In fact the technique is not to ignore the errors but to ignore those messages which contain errors. Consider a simplex transmission system using VRC which is used to transmit a list of records – these records may be a list of non-urgent orders. If records n and m are received with parity errors, but all others are received with no indication of a parity error it may be quite acceptable to process all of the 'good' orders and leave the others until some other higher-level verification takes place. This is particularly useful for:

— simplex operation;
— lists of discretely processable information;
— systems which can detect non-processed information at a later stage.

In reality the correction of the error, or perhaps more accurately the recovery from the error, is left not to a higher-level communication protocol function but to an application system function.

The most common form of error correction is to *repeat* any corrupted messages until a successful transmission has been achieved. Operating in teletype mode there are two methods by which erroneous characters may be repeated:

— character retransmission. Here the originator may backspace to the erroneous character and repeat that character and all subsequent characters. This method is only available before the message (normally a single line of input) has been terminated (by a CR or other terminator);
— message abort. In this case the entire message (again a line of input) is aborted and then repeated.

Predicting content makes use of two factors:

— the intelligence of the system (usually a human operator);
— the non-random (or predictable) nature of the information.

Consider the case of two TTY devices which are connected back-to-back across a transmission network. Transmission occurs in asynchronous character mode and error detection is by VRC. If an error is detected a special character (normally an asterisk) is printed on the output device. The human operator of the system will often be able to understand fully the original contents of the message and, in fact, the form of error correction being used (together with an amount of predicted decoding).

Consider the following example:

Transmitted text: The boy stood on the burning deck.
Printed text: The boy stood on the *urning d*ck.

A human user could translate the printed text to the original text without a great chance of making a mistake. The hidden sophistication of this system is that even if double bit-errors had occurred in this message, such that characters were translated without an error being indicated, the human user may have still been able to correct the message.

Transmitted text: The boy stood on the burning deck.
Printed text: The boy stood on the turning duck.

This system is not suitable for messages which contain non-predictive information such as sales figures, telephone numbers, etc. It is certainly not suitable for computer data transfer.

FLOW CONTROL

Flow control is particularly important for many asynchronous terminals. This is due to the stop/start nature of the transmission. It is quite common to have a print mechanism which is not capable of accepting characters at the maximum line rate. There is a small buffer which can accept a temporary overflow of several characters, but if a continuous stream arrives for any period it is necessary to use flow control.

Despite this, some asynchronous systems offer no flow control. This is acceptable only when the data can be accepted at the maximum permitted line speed for a sustained period. When flow control is provided there are two methods of achieving it. These are:

— X-ON, X-OFF;

— DTR control.

'X-ON' and 'X-OFF' are transmission control characters which are sent from a receiving terminal to an originating terminal to indicate that transmission may commence (X-ON) or must stop (X-OFF).

The term 'DTR Control' is now something of a misnomer although its original usage was correct. The method uses two of the 'V.24' interface circuits, Data Terminal Ready (DTR) and Data Set Ready (DSR) to pass flow control information between two terminals. The DTR interface circuit from the receiving terminal is connected directly to the DSR interface circuit of the transmitting terminal (both terminals being connected back-to-back without modems). When the receiving terminal wishes to enable data flow to commence it raises its DTR signal causing the DSR input to be raised at the transmitting terminal and the opposite when transmission is to stop. This technique can be extended over modem links by using any modem circuitry to carry the signal and by making suitable alterations to the terminal-to-modem cables. The flow control is thus made via the DSR circuit with the DTR circuit being only one possible source of the signal.

SUMMARY

Asynchronous TTY DLCPs have the following characteristics:

— asynchronous operation only;

— character mode transmission;

— block and file framing not provided;

— point-to-point operation only;

— full-duplex transmission required for half-duplex operation;

— error detection by VRC only;

— no error correction;

— flow control by X-ON X-OFF, or DTR control or not supplied;

— inefficient;

— not suitable for operation of clustered devices;

— simple and inexpensive to implement.

ACK/NACK ASYNCHRONOUS DLCPs

TTY-type DLCPs are suitable for use with a terminal which is emulating a teletype. They are not suitable for interconnecting automatic processes such as are found in computer systems. In order to remove the human element required during transmission (assistance may still be required to commence and terminate the session) the most important requirement is for some form of automatic error correction.

ACK/NACK protocols achieve this by transmitting the information in blocks, which are transmitted one at a time to the destination. Successful receipt of a block is then ACK'd (acknowledged) to indicate that the next block may be sent or NACK'd (negative acknowledgement) to request repeat of the suspect block. This technique is more commonly used in synchronous DLCPs and is fully described in Chapter 4.

4 Character-Structured Synchronous DLCPs

INTRODUCTION

From the summary of asynchronous DLCPs it is clear that there is 'much room for improvement'. During the early 1960s it became clear that DLCPs were required that would:

— allow flexibility of terminal configurations (ie clustering);

— allow flexibility of network configuration (ie tree networks);

— provide good error control;

— be fully automatic in operation;

— operate at high speeds.

During the same period, synchronous modems were being developed which would operate over circuits provided from the PSTN trunk networks, at greater speeds than those available from the corresponding asynchronous modems. As a result of this, a series of protocols were developed which, for reasons that will become clear, were called block mode protocols.

The development of an International Standards Organisation (ISO) synchronous block mode protocol known as the 'Basic Mode' protocol, gave a generic name to these DLCPs. The development of a subsequent generation of DLCPs which amongst other new features, permitted the transfer of unstructured strings of data (known as bit-oriented protocols) has given rise to a further name for the class of protocol discussed here, that of byte-oriented (or character-oriented) protocols. Bit-oriented protocols are discussed in Chapter 5.

PRINCIPLES OF BASIC MODE PROTOCOLS

Before explaining in detail how the various requirements of a DLCP are answered by a Basic Mode protocol it is worth considering a summary of how these protocols operate as a whole.

Basic Mode protocols operate over tree-structured networks. At the root of the tree lies the master node which controls all communication between itself and the slave nodes (no communication between slaves is permitted). The basic message element is that of the transmission block. A transmission block consists of a number of characters (or bytes).

The order of operation is that the master communicates with each slave in turn, either sending or soliciting information, a technique known as polling.

The details given in the following sections are based loosely on one such DLCP. It should be appreciated that the proprietary versions (and the ISO standard) each have minor variations from the description given in the text. It is the principle of operation which is considered to be important here. Details, if required, should always be obtained from the supplier of an individual version.

FRAMING

Character and Block Framing

The basic unit of transmission of a basic mode DLCP is the transmission block. Chapter 2 describes the way in which bit timing information is supplied with the data signal, making it not necessary to synchronise at the start of each character (unlike the case of an asynchronous interface). The method of framing used for a synchronous interface is to transmit the characters of a block sequentially without inter-character gaps such that one character follows immediately after another. Hence synchronising information is required only at the beginning of a block.

This method of block framing is achieved by sending a synchronising pattern which the receiver can lock onto. In practice this consists of a special character (SYN) which is transmitted several times in succession (usually the minimum requirement is twice). The SYN character may be repeated many times by the transmitting node and the receiving node must idle during repeat of all redundant SYNs. The information contained within the block is then begun with another special character which may be used to identify the type of block (ie data, control or supervisory). As in the case of the asynchronous DCLPs it is desirable to ensure that a block has been received in full and an end-of-block pattern is used to achieve this. In the byte mode protocol this presents no problem as certain characters may be reserved for this purpose (typically ETX, EOB, etc). A de-synchronising pattern, which instructs the receiver to begin searching for the next sequence of SYN characters then follows. This consists of the hex character FF (ie eight successive 1s).

File Delimiters

The initial unit of information to be considered was the file. As was the case with TTY protocols the beginning of a file is determined by the behavioural sequence of the protocol (ie it follows some other event). The end of a file is usually indicated by a block which is terminated with an EOT character.

LINE ACCESS CONTROL

Polling

Applying the block mode transmission systems outlined above to a simple point-to-point network there is a requirement that one of the terminals controls the transmission, with the other responding only to messages from this station. This relationship is often called master-slave (primary-secondary) and the technique is called polling. Consider the three states of the secondary; unavailable, idle or active.

Unavailable (illustrated in Figure 4.1):

1 – the master must poll the slave to determine whether or not the slave has become available since the last poll.

2 – having completed the poll, the master must wait for a response from the slave. This waiting time (Tw) must be the maximum within which the slave might reply.

3 – if the slave is unavailable (no response within Tw), the master must continue to poll the slave as in stage 1.

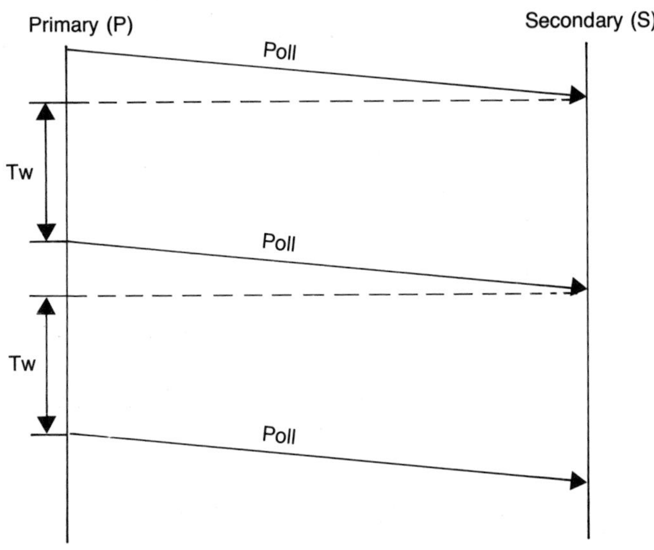

Figure 4.1 Polling of Unavailable Secondary

Available (illustrated in Figure 4.2):

1 – the master polls the slave to determine whether the slave now has data for the master, or the slave cluster (or one of its devices) has changed status (ie hold pressed on a line printer).

2 – the slave replies to the poll indicating that it has no data available and that its status remains unchanged.

3 – the master continues to poll the slave as in event 1. Note that the polling may occur at a much faster rate than in the case of the unavailable terminal as the response from the slave arrives at the master before Tw has expired.

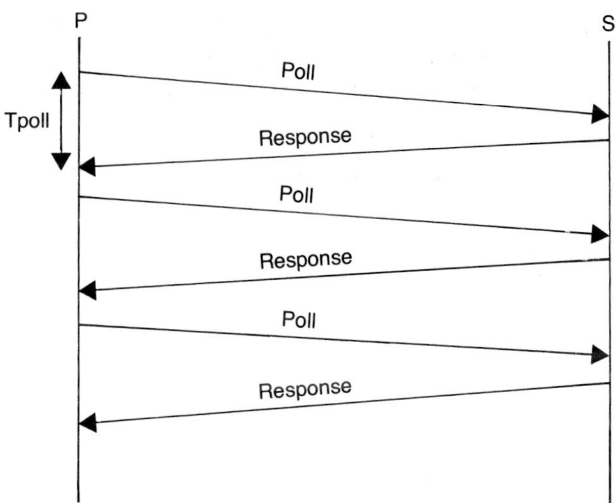

Figure 4.2 Polling of Idle Secondary

Active. There are two cases to be considered here. These are those of a master sending text to a slave and a master receiving text from a slave.

Master to slave (illustrated in Figure 4.3):

1 – the master issues a SELECT (a block containing data) to the slave. The SELECT contains the address of the device to which the text is being sent and the text itself.

2a – if the block was not the final block (ie terminated in ETB) the slave replies with an ACK or NACK as appropriate.

2b – if the block was the final block (ie terminated in EOT) the slave does not reply.

The reason that no response is made to the EOT message is that the slave would then not be aware that this response had been received by the master. Extending the number of messages provides no solution to this problem as certainty that the final message has reached its destination is never attained. For this reason the EOT block contains no data.

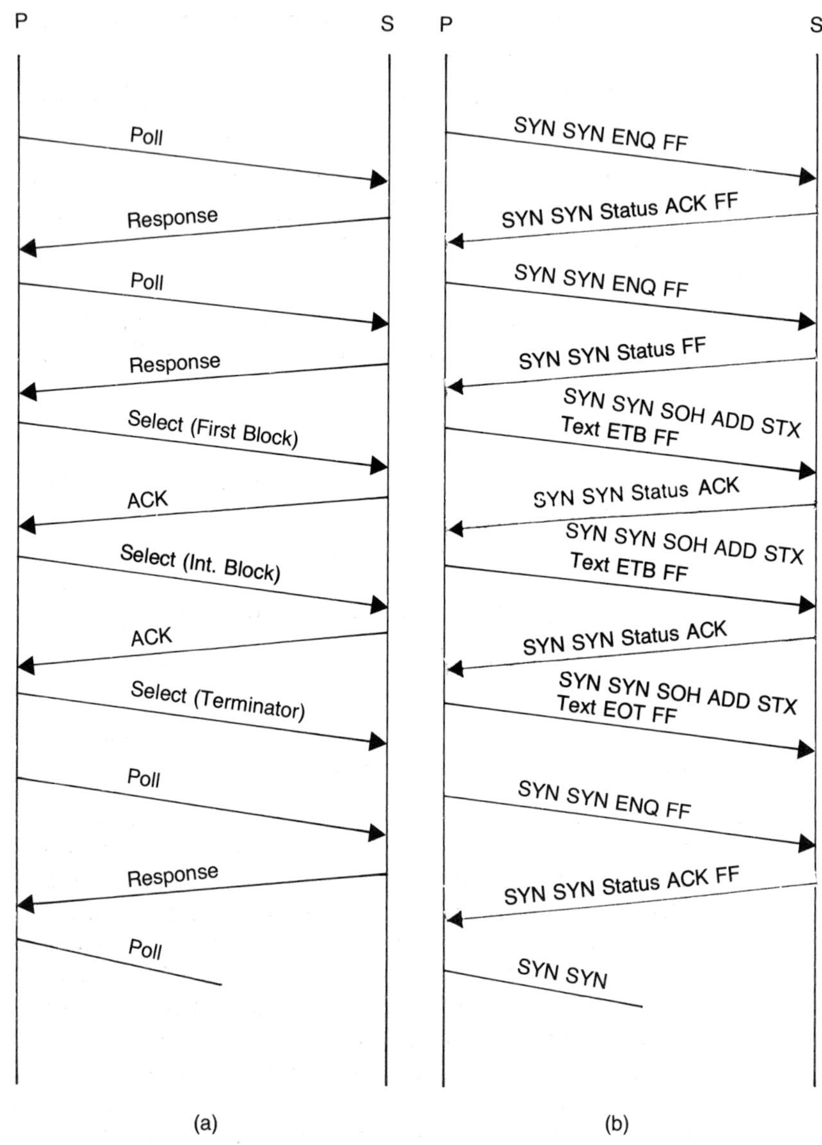

Figure 4.3 Transmission from Primary to Secondary

There are some important points to note concerning Figure 4.3 and subsequent event diagrams.

Figure 4.3 (a) shows the general terms for the events that are taking place.

Figure 4.3 (b) shows a simplified example of the actual characters being transmitted. For instance Figure 4.3 (b) shows no parity checking or block sequencing information (these will be introduced later).

The synchronising characters SYN and FF will not normally be shown in the diagrams which follow. The second case to be considered is that of:

Master from slave (illustrated in Figure 4.4):

1 – polling continues until the slave responds with 'data available'.

2 – the master permits data transfer with a data poll.

3 – the slave transmits a text block to the master.

4a – if the block was not the final block the master responds with an ACK or a NACK as appropriate.

4b – if the block was the final block the master does not respond directly but resumes polling.

We have only considered simple systems with a single communications circuit and with single-function terminals. Many transmission networks contain a number of terminal clusters and each cluster may have many devices associated with it, each device requiring autonomous connections to the host. The polling system described above is limited to one master but it is possible to have a large number of slaves. This is achieved by allocating a unique address to each cluster on any connected network. The master then includes the address of the slave cluster with which it is communicating at the beginning of each poll. When transmitting to the master the secondary includes its own address in the message if required. There are two levels of addressing:

— cluster (or group): this is the network access point address of the terminal system;

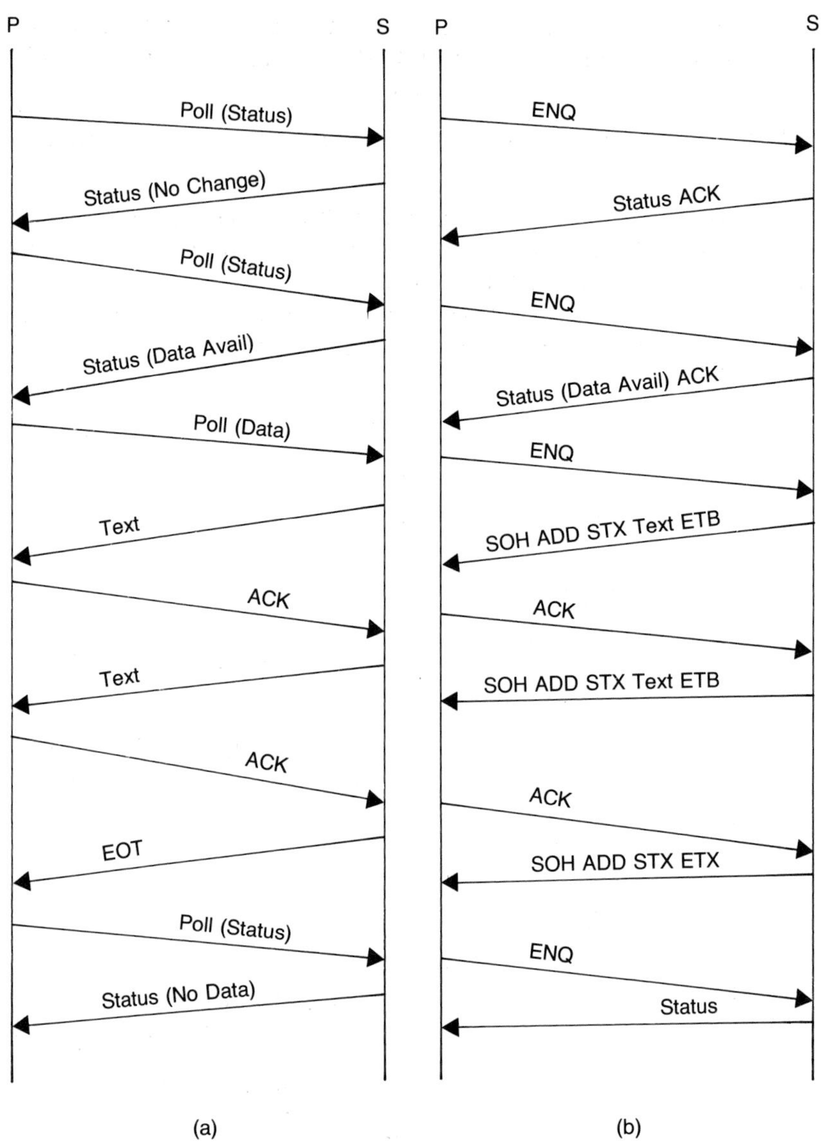

Figure 4.4 Transmission to Primary from Secondary

— unit (or tributary): this is the sub-address of a particular device within a cluster. Note that the cluster controller will have its own tributary address.

Figure 4.5 illustrates a polling system within a master and two slaves (A and B).

It should be noted that certain tributary addresses may be associated with particular types of device, ie a line printer, a card reader or a video terminal. As a result of this there is a limit not only to the maximum number of devices that may be associated with any cluster but also to the number of examples of each type of device within that one cluster.

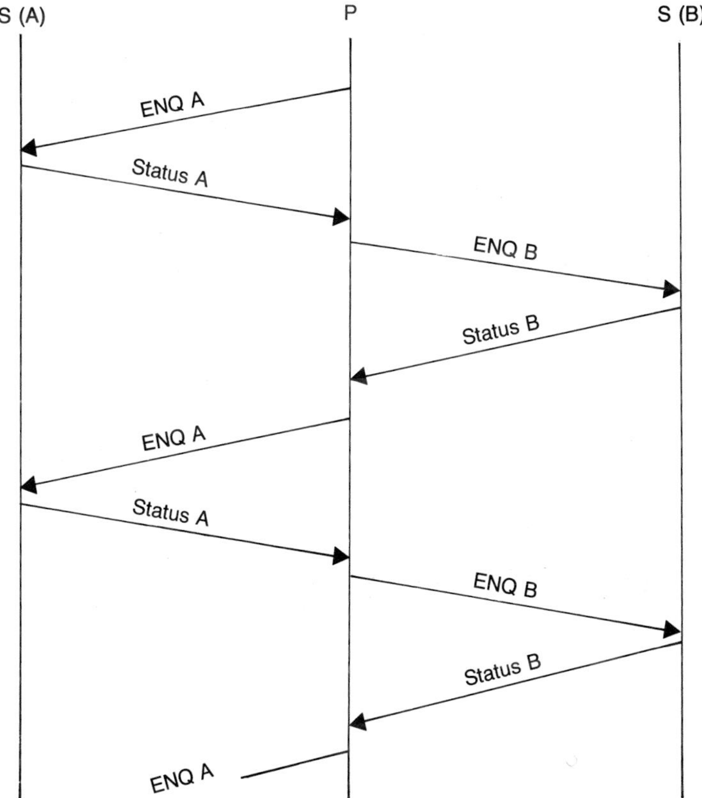

Figure 4.5 Polling Sequence – 'Master and 2 Slaves'

The major advantage of a two-tier addressing scheme can be seen in the case of a cluster for which all devices are idle. The master may send a single poll to the cluster controller which replies that there is no data available from any device within that cluster. In this way the need to poll each device individually is removed, and line access control is maintained by the master.

In practice, systems have some refinements to the system as outlined above, one of the most important being that of weighted polling. Under this scheme, terminals within the system may be polled at different rates which are either pre-set to reflect their activity levels and required response times, or are dynamically altered to reflect their current activity. An example of the former case is that a cluster containing an on-line enquiry terminal may be polled more often than one which contains only a card reader and a printer. The second case is implemented in most proprietary protocols and is designed to reduce the amount of time which is spent waiting for replies to polls to unavailable devices. The timeout period (Tw in Figure 4.1) is much greater than the normal value of a poll cycle (Tpoll in Figure 4.2). In a network with many slave clusters of which some are available and some are unavailable the time between successive polls to the same device will be kept high, due largely to the time spent in Tw's. Weighted polling ensures that several cycles of polls are sent to available terminals before any are sent to unavailable terminals. An example of weighted polling is illustrated in Figure 4.6.

VARIATIONS (CONTENTION AND CONVERSATIONAL MODE)

There are two drawbacks to the polling system which may be addressed.

Contention

Any terminal must be configured to behave as a master or a slave. If it is necessary to establish a connection between two terminals via a temporary network connection (such as a dial-up telephone circuit) it is necessary to ensure that one of the terminals is configured as a primary and the other as a secondary. Where this temporary connection may be made between only two terminals one

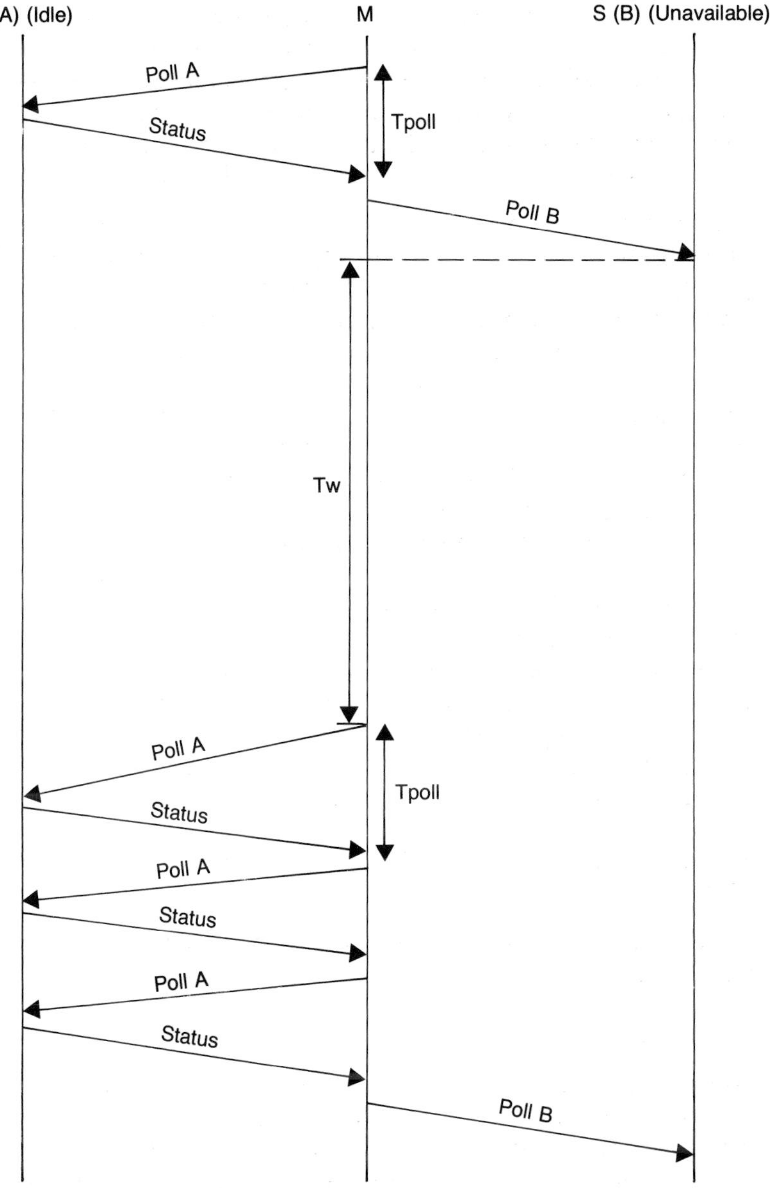

Figure 4.6 Weighted Polling

can be permanently allocated as a master and the other as a slave. If, however, there are three or more terminals, with communication required between any two, this arrangement no longer holds, ie if terminal A is a primary then terminals B and C must be secondaries if they need to communicate with A. Then terminals B and C will not be able to communicate with each other.

The solution to this problem is available by using a link session initialisation procedure known as contention. This is suitable for point-to-point operation only and operates as follows. In the idle state both terminals assume slave status and hence no polling takes place. When one of the terminals wishes to transmit to the other it assumes master status and issues a poll to the other. The normal transmission procedures may then continue. This is illustrated in Figure 4.7 (terminal A transmits to terminal B).

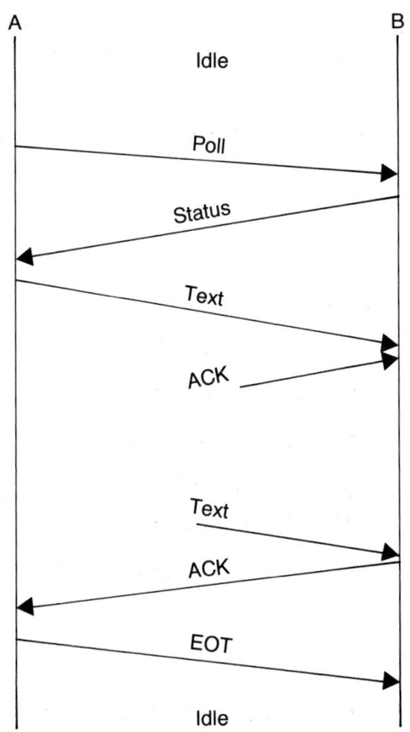

Figure 4.7 Contention in Operation

Conversational Mode

This may be used where there is a frequent exchange of relatively short messages such as in an interactive or conversational environment. Under normal operation the ACK/NACK messages would absorb a significant amount of available line time. Conversational mode allows ACKs to be replaced with an information message, the STX or SOH effectively replacing the ACK message. If a NACK is required this must be transmitted as normal.

ERROR CONTROL

General

We have already described the error control systems which are available for asynchronous DLCPs. The type of parity error system used there utilised VRC (or character parity checking) to generate the parity information. This technique together with the similar LRC (see below) system is generally applied to Basic Mode transmission blocks.

The method of error control used for Basic Mode transmission operates as follows:

— transmit a block;

— check if block received without errors *

— reply to original block with ACK if no errors or
with NACK if there are errors;

— if no errors repeat process for next block;

— if there are errors repeat process with corrupted block;

— if the number of retransmissions for a single block exceeds a set limit, abandon transmission.

* as has already been stated, it is not possible to devise a system which will detect all errors.

Error Detection

The method of generating parity information most commonly used in Basic Mode protocols is that of VRC and LRC. VRC was described in detail in Chapter 3. It was pointed out that this system is not very reliable as any even number of errors occurring in a single character will not be detected. An improvement to this system is offered by LRC.

Longitudinal (or Lateral) Redundancy Checking (LRC)

One method of improving the resilience of VRC systems is that of LRC. LRC sums the total value of all of the first bits of each character within a transmission data block. A parity bit is then determined as in VRC and this parity bit is used to form the first bit of a 'parity' character. The same procedure is followed for the second bit of each character and so on until a complete parity character has been calculated. This character is then transmitted at the end of a transmission block. It is normal practice to include VRC on each character when LRC is used. The general 'convention' is to perform odd parity VRC and even parity LRC in this case. An example of such a system is illustrated below. By grouping characters into blocks it is possible to describe the bit pattern as a matrix as shown in Figure 4.8. Note that the parity character always has itself the correct vertical redundancy check.

Despite being a great improvement on VRC only systems it is still possible to have an undetected error with only four corrupted bits. If two bits are corrupted in any single character and the corresponding two bits are also corrupted in another character, then the error detection process will fail. This is illustrated in Figure 4.9.

Cyclic Redundancy Checking (CRC)

A further method of parity error information generation which may be applied to block mode protocols is known as Cyclic Redundancy Checking (CRC). This technique is described fully in Chapter 5 (Bit-Oriented Protocols).

END-TO-END SYNCHRONISATION

Up to this point it has been assumed that each message sent by either the source or sink was received and recognised by its recipient. There are two events which would prevent this from happening:

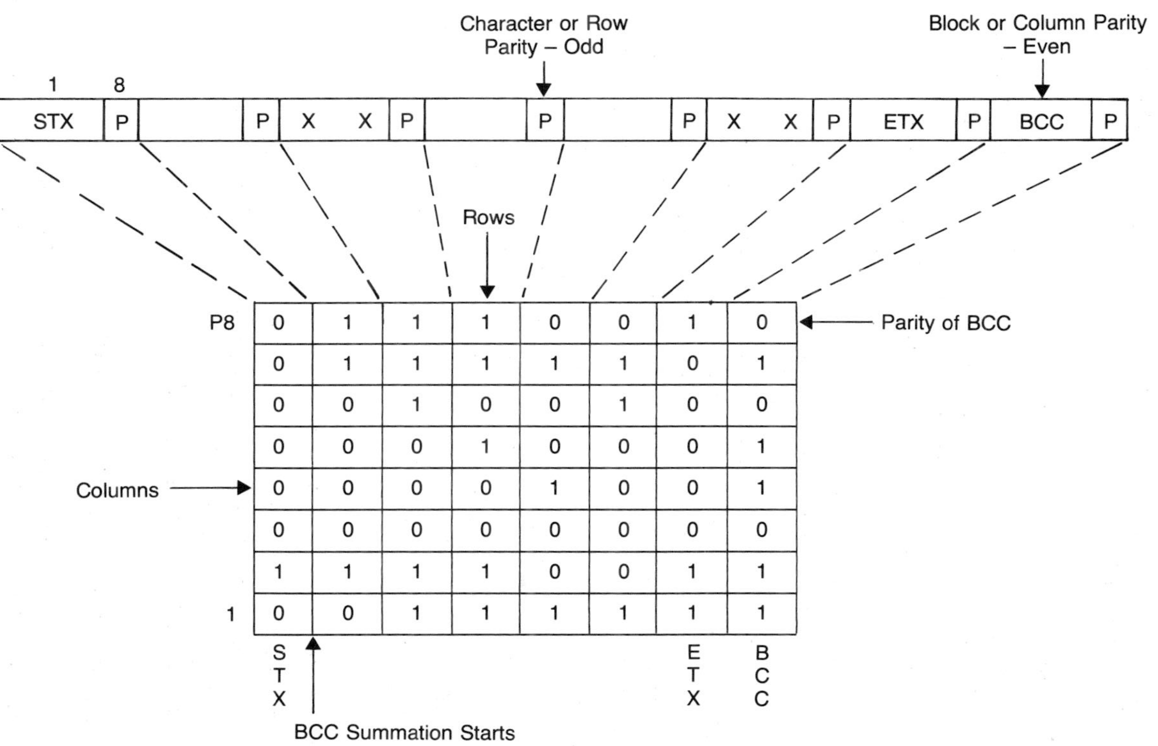

Figure 4.8 Vertical and Longitudinal Parity Checks

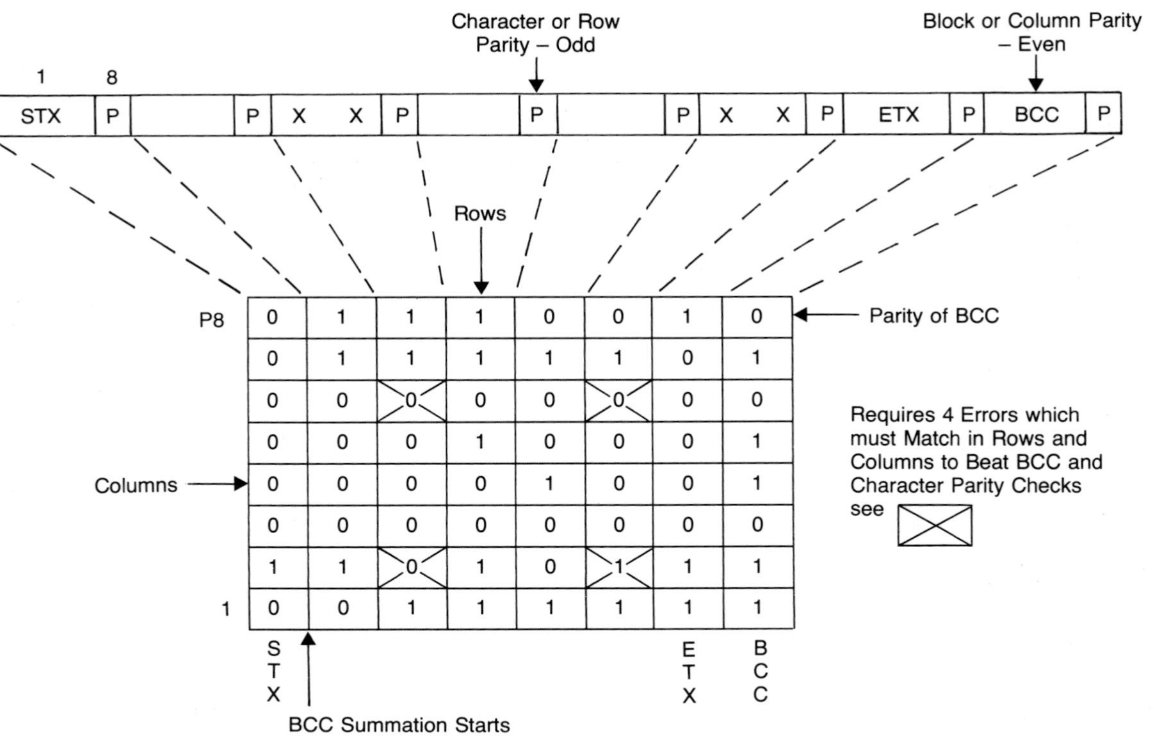

Figure 4.9 VRC/CRC Failure

— a message may be 'lost' within the network and not reach the recipient;

— a message may be so badly corrupted that it is not recognised by the recipient as being a message.

Although both of the scenarios given above have the same effect there are two stages in the procedure during which this might happen:

— the transmitted block is lost;

— a response (ie ACK/NACK) is lost.

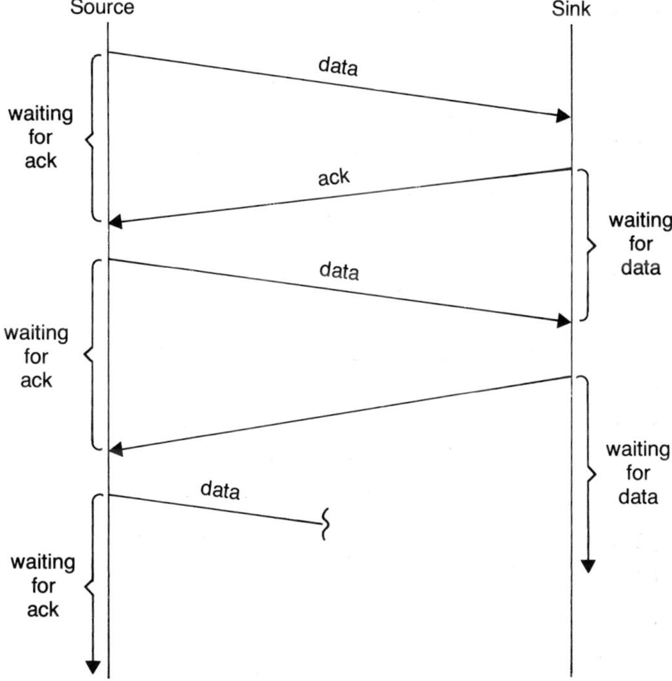

Figure 4.10 Terminal States after Lost Transmission Block

Consider the first case (lost transmission block). This is illustrated in Figure 4.10. After a block is lost the source and sink are in the following states:

— source has transmitted a valid block, and does not know whether the sink has received the message and responded (with an ACK or a NACK) or whether the sink has not received the message;

— sink has transmitted a valid response, and does not know whether the source received this response and responded with the next transmission block (which was lost) or whether the initial response was lost.

The protocol is now in a state where neither source nor sink is aware of the state of the other and two actions are necessary:

— restart transmission;

— ensure that source and sink are synchronised within two transmission blocks (ie no block has been missed out and no block has been duplicated).

The method by which this problem may be overcome is as follows:

— provide a time-out period after which recovery procedure is initiated;

— provide sequencing information with each block and response;

— provide recovery procedure.

After transmitting a message, a master station expects a reply within a predetermined time. If it does not receive any reply after such a period it will retransmit that message, this is known as a 'retry'. If after a specified number of retries (typically three to fifteen) there is still no response, the transmission may be abandoned and status polling resumed.

The method by which message sequence is ensured is to provide a sequence number with each data block and acknowledgement (positive or negative). In the case where each message block is acknowledged before another is sent it is only necessary to provide two distinct sequence numbers and to toggle between them (ie block 0, block 1, block 0, block 1, etc).

We shall now follow the procedures and facilities described above in examples.

Consider the case of a master transmitting information to a slave. There are two possible scenarios for a lost message:

— lost transmission block;

— lost response.

The case of a lost transmission block is illustrated in Figure 4.11. After the transmission block is lost the states of the terminals are as follows:

master: waiting for an ack 0

slave: waiting for a block 0

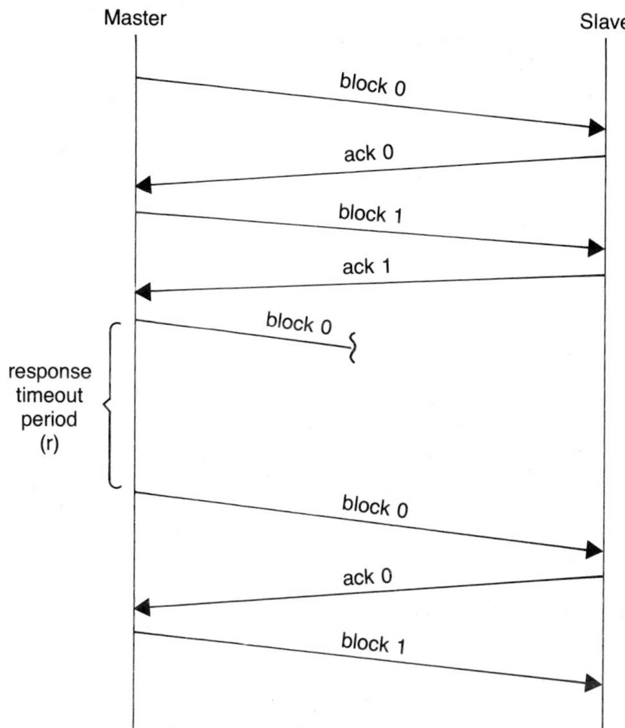

Figure 4.11 Lost Master Transmission Block

The response timeout period 'r' then elapses and the master retransmits the block 0. The slave then receives the expected block and transmission continues as normal.

The case of a lost response is illustrated in Figure 4.12. After the response is lost the states of the terminals are similar to the case above:

master: waiting for an ack 0

slave: waiting for a block 1

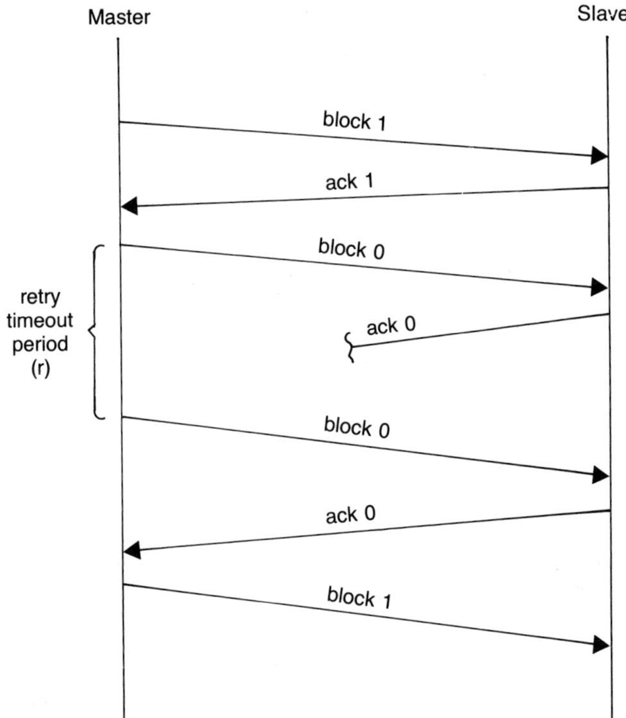

Figure 4.12 Lost Slave Response

Again the response timeout period elapses and the master retransmits the last block. This time the slave receives a block with an unexpected sequence number. The slave, assuming that a retry has occurred, ignores the user content of this block, but repeats the acknowledgement. Thus the transmission sequence has been maintained and the session may continue.

Now consider the case of the slave transmitting information to the master. Again there are two scenarios to consider:

— a lost response;

— a lost transmission block.

The case of the lost response (this time a master-originated message) is illustrated in Figure 4.13. After the response is lost the states of the terminals are as follows:

master: waiting for block 1

slave: waiting for ack 0

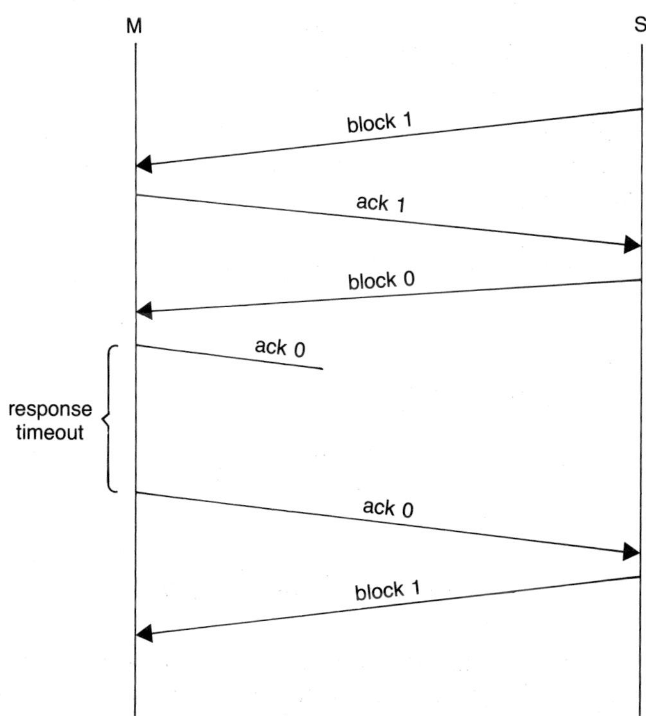

Figure 4.13 Lost Master Response

Again the response timeout at the master terminal is exceeded and the master retransmits the ack 0. As this is the message that the slave is expecting, the transmission can continue as normal.

The case of the lost transmission block is illustrated in Figure 4.14. After loss of the message the state of the terminals is as follows:

master: waiting for block 0

slave: waiting for an ack 0

The timeout period expires and the master retransmits the ack 1. The secondary recognises that this is a repeat ack and therefore deduces that the previous transmission block was lost. It therefore repeats the previous block 0 and order is once again restored.

This form of sequence control is known as 'stop and wait' operation, as after each message is transmitted the source must stop and wait for a response. It is rather inefficient as user data is only being transmitted for a fraction of line availability time. The system operates in half-duplex mode although it may of course be implemented over transmission circuits which have full-duplex capability.

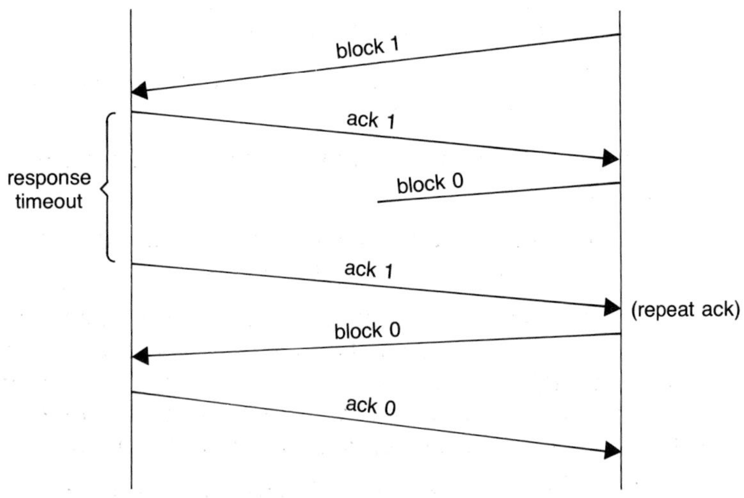

Figure 4.14 Lost Slave Block

LIMITATIONS OF CHARACTER OR LIMITED PROTOCOLS

Despite the fact that character-oriented protocols have served the data communications requirements for well over a decade they clearly suffer from a number of limitations. Some of these have already been mentioned in the text but the following section provides a summary of these and some (although not necessarily all) others:

— master/slave relationship is inherent in the protocol;

— they are oriented to a centrally-controlled system;

— a number of different block types are required for various purposes such as:

  — information transfer;
  — positive acknowledgement;
  — negative acknowledgement;
  — request for retransmission;
  — busy indication (ie inability to process further information transfers at present).

The protocol is designed around the transfer of characters, messages, and to some extent, files. Ideally these three distinctions should be reserved for higher-level functions.

— additional procedures are required to transfer binary data or non-standard characters;

— over protection is restricted to the data field whereas block headers are unprotected;

— operation is in half-duplex stop-and-wait mode making inefficient use of transmission resources.

The limitations of Basic Mode protocols has been apparent since their introduction indicating that they were not as severe as the length of the list might suggest. Nevertheless a second generation of synchronous DLCPs was developed which overcame many of these restrictions. These are discussed in the next chapter.

The techniques described in this section have been used in many proprietary datalink protocols. Unfortunately for the user the combination of message format, line control, error control and flow control chosen are modified by each supplier (often with several different versions per supplier) and there is no protocol for requirements. However, the techniques used are similar to those described above and this section is now completed with a list of some, but by no means all, Basic Mode DLCPs.

These protocols include:

— ISO Basic Mode Protocol;

— IBM Binary Synchronous Communications (BISYNC or BSC);

— ICL C01, C02, C03;

— Dec DDCMD;

— Univac U200;

— CDC 200UT;

— Burroughs Multipoint Poll Select.

5 Bit-Oriented Protocols

INTRODUCTION

One of the final sections of the last chapter indicated that a second generation of DLCPs had been developed which answered many of the criticisms aimed at the Basic Mode protocols. This family is that of the bit-oriented protocols based around the ISO High-Level Data Link Control (HDLC) and the similar ANSI-ADCCP (Advanced Data Communication Control Protocol) procedures. Indeed many of the proprietary versions use a sub-set of the full HDLC protocol. It should be clearly recognised that the phrase 'High Level' has become something of a misnomer, as it is a link-level protocol and not a high-level protocol in the now normally accepted use of the term. This is not indicative of any pretention on behalf of the designers of HDLC. Rather, it results from the adoption of the term to describe other types of protocol after it had already been applied to HDLC. When originally conceived, HDLC was indeed a 'high level' protocol, compared with those in existence at that time.

This chapter provides details of the concepts, structure and operation of HDLC. An understanding of these will arm the reader with information which may be applied to all such protocols.

The essential features of HDLC such as the frame structure and its nested construction or 'onion skin' architecture had their origins in the work of a British Standards Institution (BSI) Committee in 1968. The BSI ideas were taken up within ISO and resulted in the standardisation by the ISO of a sophisticated method of data-link control, known as HDLC.

The HDLC standards are much sounder, as standards, than the earlier Basic Mode standards. They were evolved by what is termed 'prospective standardisation' which is the planning of standards before many conflicting systems became established on the market (despite this there are still several 'proprietary' variants which are available). Taken together they form a powerful and sophisticated group of facilities, which are very widely used. Although they have a great versatility to cover a wide spectrum of applications, at their core lies a relatively simple set of procedures; for the majority of systems these will suffice and will thus readily permit interworking (at least at the data link level).

OVERVIEW

The HDLC family has the following characteristics:

— HDLC was originally designed for two-way simultaneous operation between a primary and one or more secondary stations on a tree network. No provision is made for secondaries to communicate with each other. Thus one of the so-called restrictions of the Basic Mode procedures remains!

— the primary station is responsible for scheduling the data flow in the link by authorising secondaries to transmit. This may be on a single message basis or for an unspecified period which may then be terminated by the primary;

— all transmissions are in 'frames';

— frames issued by a primary station are referred to as 'commands' and frames issued by a secondary terminal are referred to as 'responses';

— a homogeneous enveloping format (one frame structure for all messages) is employed;

— the information field of a frame is of variable length;

— frames may be transmitted whilst previous frames are still awaiting acknowledgement;

— error control is applied to all frames (Basic Mode offers protection to information blocks only).

— error control is applied to all of the frame (Basic Mode frames have error control on data fields only);

— transmission is bit oriented which means that any sequence of bits can be transmitted in the information field of a frame.

There are three components to the HDLC standard:

— the frame structure;

— the elements of the procedure;

— the classes of procedure.

The first specifies the common 'frame structure', including the error checking and bit sequence transparency mechanisms and the size and position of the Address and Control fields.

The 'Elements of Procedure' specify the commands, the responses and the sequencing information which can be coded into the control field for link control and error recovery purposes. The 'Classes of Procedure' define various modes of operation of a link (master-master, master-slave etc); each class uses an appropriate selection of the commands and responses defined in the elements of procedure.

HDLC FRAME

General

One of the main characteristics of HDLC is the 'homogeneous enveloping format'. This single transmission frame format is used to achieve both information and control interchange. The general format of a frame is shown in Figure 5.1.

Frame delimiting is provided by means of a unique octet coded as '01111110' which is called the flag sequence F. The F field appears at the beginning and end of each frame, although the end F of one frame may also act as the beginning F of the next frame. The requirement that this sequence remains unique to the F field demands that a special mechanism is provided to prevent it from occurring in the other fields. This is discussed more fully below. The other fields in a frame are detected by their position relative to these delimiting flags.

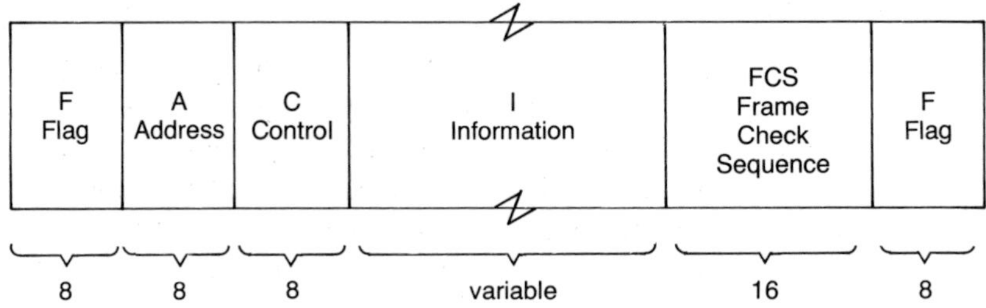

Figure 5.1 HDLC Frame Format

The address octet (A), the first octet of the first region, defines the address, local to the communications link on which the frame is travelling, to which the frame is destined or from where it originated. This permits a maximum of 256 terminals to be connected by means of a single link. The address field of a command carries the address of the terminal for which that command is intended. The address field of a response carries the address of the terminal which is responding. This permits a primary to identify the source of the response.

The control octet (C), the second octet of the first region, defines the type of command or response carried by the frame. Three types of frame are defined and each has its own control field format. This is discussed more fully below.

The information field (I) is the third region described above. It is unrestricted in structure and length. Indeed it may have zero length in certain frames but by always considering that it exists the homogeneous nature of the frame structure is maintained. HDLC protocols will always be concerned with the transportation of this region between communicating parties but will not be concerned with the content of this region. To that extent it may be considered to be of undefined structure in terms of HDLC protocols.

The Frame Check Sequence (FCS) is the sixteen bit (normally) sequence which carries the parity error check information as determined by CRC parity generation. The sequence may also be referred to as the protection bits.

Frame Delimiting

There are three aspects to the delimiting of HDLC frames. The first is the identification of the beginning of a frame. As explained above this is indicated by the receipt of the flag sequence F. The second is the identification of an end of frame and this again is determined by the receipt of a flag sequence. The third aspect is that of the identification of the fields with a frame. This is achieved as follows:

— the address field consists of the first eight bits received after the initial F sequence;

— the control field consists of the eight bits which follow immediately after the A field;

— the FCS field consists of the sixteen bits which immediately precede the second F sequence;

— the I field is of variable length and consists of all bits between the C and the FCS fields.

There are two conflicting requirements inherent in this system:

1) The frame must be capable of transporting any sequence of bits;

2) The first sequence of bits which corresponds to the F sequence, which is detected after the opening flag, will be taken to be the closing flag. In other words the F sequence cannot be allowed to appear in the frame other than as the F field.

The mechanism by which this is achieved is known as the 'transparency mechanism' and the technique used to achieve this is referred to as 'bit stuffing'. Implementation is by means of a relatively simple algorithm. At the transmitter the number of consecutive ones is counted and whenever an unbroken sequence of five ones is detected, other than in the F sequence, the transmitter inserts a zero into the bit stream. At the receiver a zero following a sequence of five ones is stripped out (often referred to as bit stripping). Then the only transmitted sequences which will contain six consecutive ones are the F sequences. Note also that as this procedure takes place after the FCS has been generated it is not subject to the error checking procedures described below.

HDLC Frame Types

Three frame types are defined within HDLC. They are grouped according to function and each group has its own control field format. They are known as I-type, S-type and U-type frames.

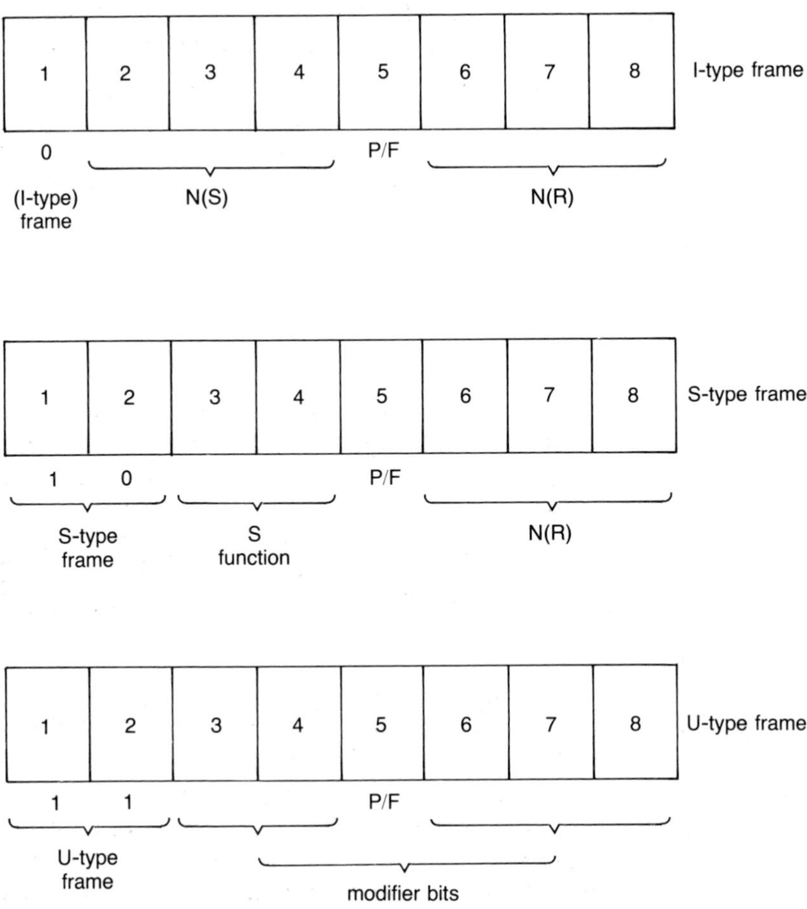

Figure 5.2 Control-Field Formats

Figure 5.2 illustrates the format of the control fields of each type. The details of the use of each element within the frames will become clear as the reader progresses through this chapter.

I-type frames perform 'information' transfer between terminals and each frame is numbered according to a cyclic numbering convention.

S-type frames perform 'supervisory' link-control functions and have an empty I field. In general they are used when there is no data available which would otherwise allow an I-type frame to be transmitted or when status information must be exchanged.

U-type or 'unnumbered' frames are used to provide additional link control information such as to bootstrap a link to an initially usable level and also when protocol errors are detected. The frames do not normally carry any I field information but may do so when diagnostic information is being provided after a protocol error has been detected.

OPERATING MODES

Levels

There are essentially two levels of operating mode which are defined within HDLC. The first applies to the structure and operation of the network itself and is called the 'class of procedure'. The second is the 'mode of operation' of the terminals themselves within that network configuration. This refers to the behaviour of individual terminals attached to the transmission network. The two levels (ie class and mode of operation) are necessarily related.

Class of Procedure

Two classes of procedure are defined for HDLC. These are 'unbalanced class' and 'balanced class'.

In the unbalanced class the network consists of a single primary station and one or more secondary stations (ie a tree network). The primary station is responsible for the initiation and termination of communications sessions between itself and each of the secondary stations on the network.

In the balanced class of procedures the link consists of two equal stations (ie a point-to-point network only). The station at either end of the link may initiate, control and terminate communications sessions.

Under either class above an individual link (primary to a secondary) may be in one of two states. These are:

— active, holding a communications session;

— idle, not holding a communications session.

Modes of Operation

Within HDLC the 'mode of operation' governs the right of a terminal to transmit information, ie it provides the line-access control mechanism.

In the Normal Response Mode (NRM) a secondary may initiate transmission only after it has received a poll from a primary station. After the transmission is complete, or the limit of the authorisation has been reached, the secondary must not continue transmission until the primary issues further approval. NRM is therefore used in the unbalanced class of procedure.

In Asynchronous Response Mode (ARM) either terminal may commence transmission without receiving authorisation from the other. Hence ARM is used in the balanced class of procedure.

In contrast to the 'response' modes, a terminal may assume, or be placed in a Disconnected Mode (NDM or ADM as appropriate). Whilst in this mode the secondary should not act upon any I-frames received or transmit any outstanding I-frames to the primary. The secondary should still accept command frames and hence can be brought out of this mode by the appropriate 'set mode' command. Both of these disconnected states may be set in a secondary by a primary by means of the DISC (Disconnect) command. A secondary may request that a primary places the secondary in disconnected mode by issuing an RD (Request Disconnect) response to a primary poll.

A final mode of operation to be considered is that of the IM (Initialisation Mode). In this mode the secondary's link control parameters are reset to their initial values.

MESSAGE SEQUENCING

HDLC is designed to operate efficiently over full-duplex circuits, ie in full-duplex mode. Rather than send a specific frame to carry each acknowledgement HDLC uses an implicit acknowledgement procedure. There are two elements of the control field which serve as the acknowledgement mechanism on the link:

— N (S – send) is the sequence number of outgoing frames. It is present in the I-type frame only. A window size of 7 is normally used so that the frames will be numbered sequentially from 0 through to 7 and then continue at 0. Note that the window size is necessarily one less than the capacity of the cycle bits (which is 8 in this case);

— N (R – receive) is the number of the next frame which the device expects to receive. N (R) is present in both I- and S-type frames. There is then an implicit acknowledgement that frames numbered to R–1 have been successfully received. Note that it is not necessary to acknowledge every received frame. If frame 2 is acknowledged (ie N (R) = 3) and then frame 6 is acknowledged (ie N (R) = 7) then frames 3, 4 and 5 are also considered to have been received without indication of error. This is illustrated in Figure 5.3. Note that for clarity the command and response frames are shown as not overlapping. In practice, when both primary and secondary are issuing I-type frames time overlapping will occur. This does not effect the procedure described. In this example, frame 4 acknowledges receipt of frames 1, 2 and 3 and frame 9 acknowledges receipt of frames 5, 6, 7 and 8.

Normally, in full-duplex information transfer, the information frames carry the relevant acknowledgements. However, if the protocol is used in a half-duplex situation, or there is no I-frame available in a full-duplex situation, then a supervisory frame (S-type) is sent instead. The frame used for this purpose is the RR (Receive Ready) frame. Such frames are not themselves numbered but carry the same N (R) as would have been the case had an I-frame been available. Figure 5.4 illustrates the use of the RR frame in this context.

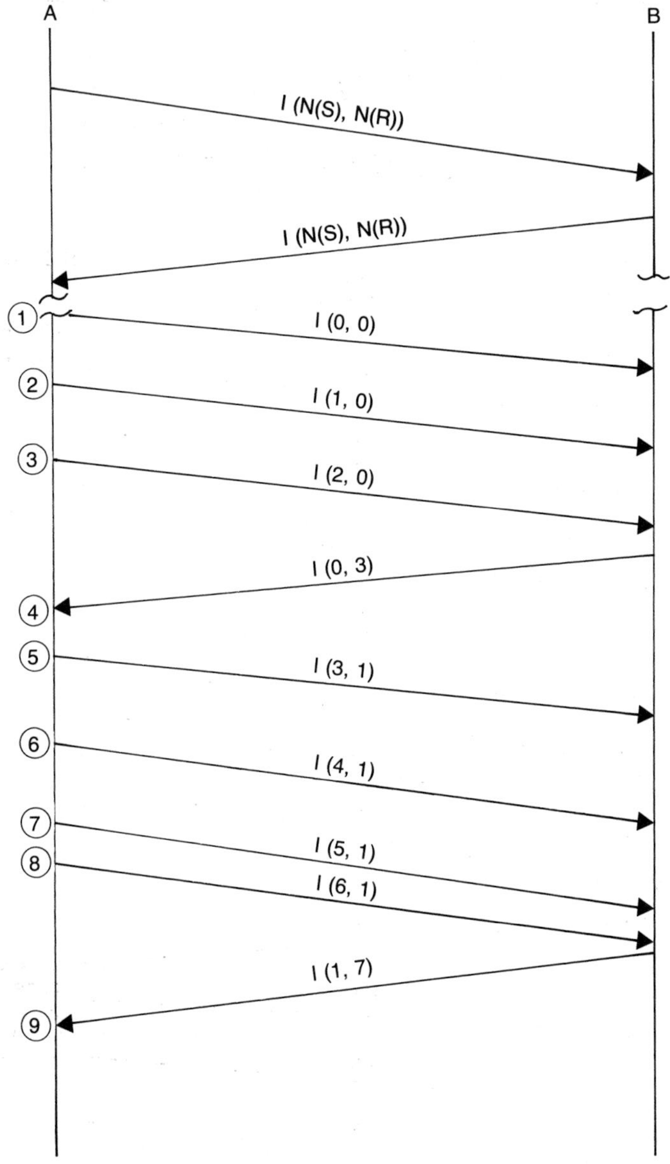

Figure 5.3 Implicit Acknowledgement of Frames

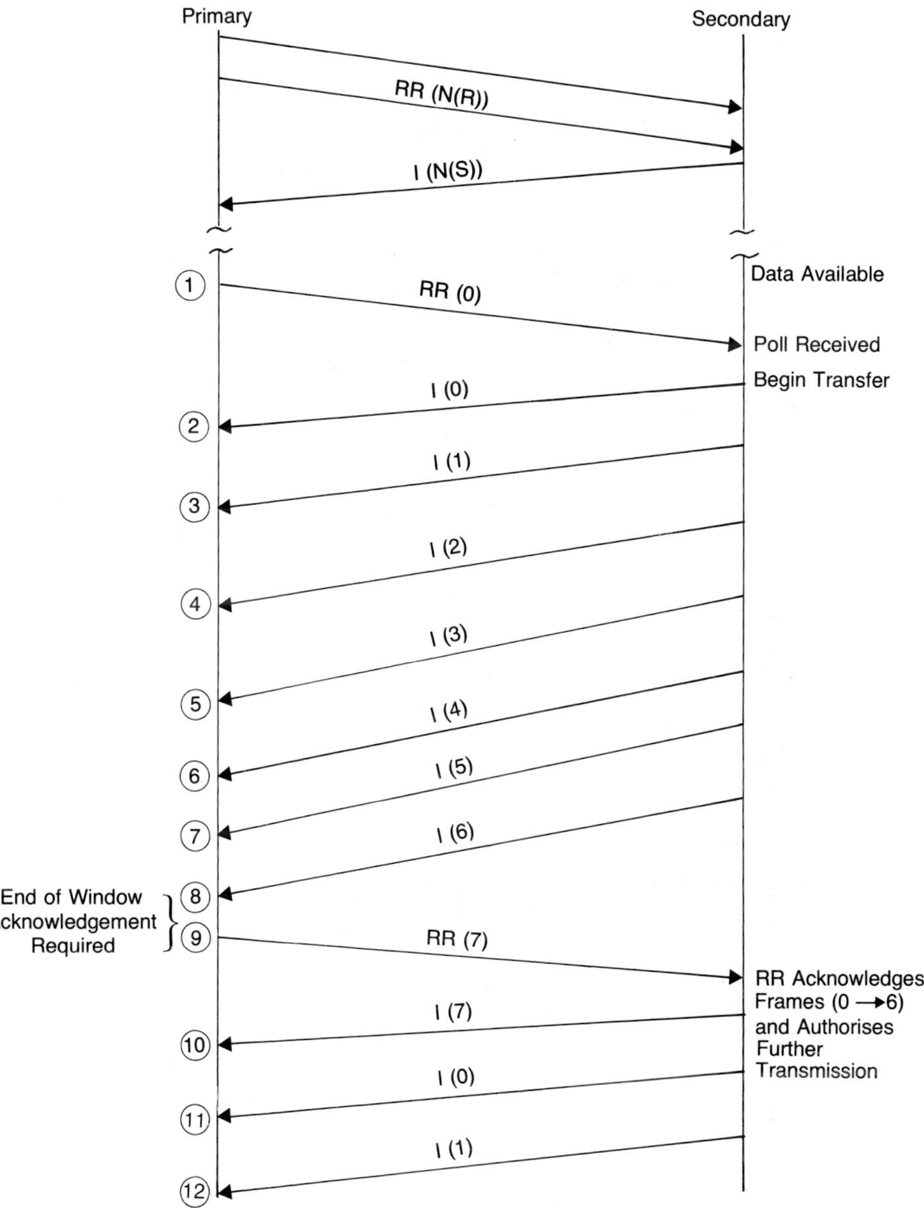

Figure 5.4 Use of RR for Acknowledgement

The significance of the frames depicted in Figure 5.4 is as follows:

1) RR, authorises secondary to transmit up to seven frames;

2–7) I-frames, window limit not yet reached;

8) I-frame, window limit reached;

9) RR, acknowledges receipt of frames 2 to 8; primary has counted the number of I-frames received, and as this equals window size assumes that there is more information in this file; authorises secondary to transmit another seven frames (max);

10–11) I-frames, note that N(S) cycles from 7 to 0.

The multi-frame transmission capability described above considerably improves the efficiency of the traditional polling operation since a single polling command can clear several queued messages from a terminal. This may be contrasted with the Basic Mode protocols which enforce a poll per queued message discipline. Obviously the overall efficiency will depend on whether the terminals are capable of buffering more than a single message. An additional factor which must be considered is the line error rate which will influence the effectiveness of sending several messages without relation to acknowledgement.

Usually the standard frame-numbering sequence, which permits a maximum of seven frames to be outstanding (ie awaiting acknowledgement), will satisfy system requirements. However, there are certain circumstances when this will be insufficient to ensure high transmission efficiency. Consider the case of a transmission system which includes one (or perhaps more) satellite hops. In this case it may be necessary to be able to support many received frames before an acknowledgement may be provided. Indeed any transmission system which has one or more of the following may require extended frame numbering;

— long propagation delay;

— high bit transfer rates;

— very short blocks.

To cater for this requirement, an extended frame numbering sequence, which permits up to 127 frames to be outstanding has been defined. The commands for invoking this option are described below.

The RR frame is also used for two other purposes. The first is by the primary to control information transfer from a secondary station as described below. The second purpose is to indicate that a terminal has (in the case of a primary) or should (in the case of a secondary) move from the RNR (Receive Not Ready) to the RR state. The use of the RNR frame is described below.

As implied by their name, unnumbered functions (U-type frames) do not carry any frame sequence number. This is primarily because they may be used during an initialisation phase. One of the objectives of such commands is to initialise the frame numbering cycle in a predetermined manner. Clearly if such frames were numbered it would be extremely difficult to define a procedure to operate effectively in all possible situations. One specific case, that of recovering after a link failure, illustrates this point very well.

Following the failure, it may have been necessary to reinitialise one terminal completely, thereby losing the stored knowledge of the current position in the frame-numbering sequence. As a result, sending an initialisation request could cause the acknowledgement mechanism to repeat an arbitary number of frames. Alternatively, a protocol error would be detected and signalled by the recipient of such a command and a more complicated recovery procedure might then be required. Thus it is clear to see that an unnumbered sequence is the best solution to this problem, since it is then possible to define a simple recovery procedure that will operate in all situations.

In order to acknowledge unnumbered commands, there is a requirement for the Unnumbered Acknowledgement (UA) response. In order that the unnumbered mechanism operates effectively it is necessary to enforce strictly the restriction that only one such command may be outstanding at any time. If this were not enforced it would not be possible to correlate commands and acknowledgements, resulting in an ambiguous state.

ACCESS CONTROL

The mechanism by which a secondary is authorised to transmit frames is by use of the poll/final (P/F) bit (bit 5 of the control field). In command frames it is known as the P-bit and in response frames it is known as the F-bit. A restriction is enforced whereby only one command frame with the P-bit set may be be issued before a response with the F-bit set is received. If the command frame is an S- or U-type then the secondary must set the F-bit on the response.

When a primary wishes to authorise transmission of I-frames from a secondary it sends the secondary either an I-type frame or an RR frame, with the P-bit set. The I-frame is used if the primary has information to send to the secondary and the RR frame is sent if not. On receiving either of these frames the secondary is authorised to transmit as many messages as it is allowed within the context of the frame-numbering and window schemes (ie normally seven).

The secondary must then set the F-bit on the last message in the sequence to indicate to the primary that a new command carrying frame acknowledgement is required before further transmission will be initiated. This may be due to one of two reasons:

— the last frame in the sequence has been transmitted;

— the outstanding message limit (window) has been reached and an acknowledgement is required before further frames may be sent.

Note that the 'message sequence' is a logical break of information made by the terminal. It may be an individual file, etc. Indicating that a message sequence has been completed does not indicate that the terminal has transmitted all of the waiting information. A terminal may have several sequences awaiting transmission. The distinction between the two conditions (ie end-of-window and end-of-sequence) is made on the basis of the number of frames received since the last authorisation.

The secondary may not transfer any more I-frames until it receives further authorisation (in the form of an I-frame or RR frame with P-bit set).

The primary will acknowledge receipt of the frames with an I-frame or RR frame as appropriate. If the primary wishes to authorise further I-frames from the secondary, it will set the P-bit in that frame. If the primary does not wish to authorise any further I-frames from that secondary, at least at that time, it will acknowledge receipt of the received frames with the P-bit clear.

By issuing I- or RR frames with the P-bit set or clear, the primary can control transmission of I-frames from a number of secondaries on a tree network. Figure 5.5 illustrates the use of the P-bit to control transmission from two secondary stations.

Note that although the command frames will be transmitted to both secondaries Figure 5.5 only shows the transmissions that will be accepted by each secondary terminal. The frames of Figure 5.5 have the following significance:

1) RR, P-set; solicits I-frames from B;

2–3) I-frames, F-clear;

4) I-frame, F-set; end of file;

5) RR, P-clear; acknowledges frames 2–5, prohibits further I-frames;

6) RR, P-set; solicits information from A;

7) I-frame, F-clear;

8) I-frame, F-set; end of file; the primary now has information to send to A;

9) I-frame, P-clear; acks frames 7–8, sends information to A, declines further I-frames from A;

10) RR, P-set; invites I-frames from A;

11) I-frame, F-clear;

12) I-frame, F-set; end of file;

13) RR, P-clear, acks 11–12, declines further I-frames;

14) I-frame, P-set; sends information to a, solicits I-frames from A;

15) I-frame, P-clear; sends information to A;

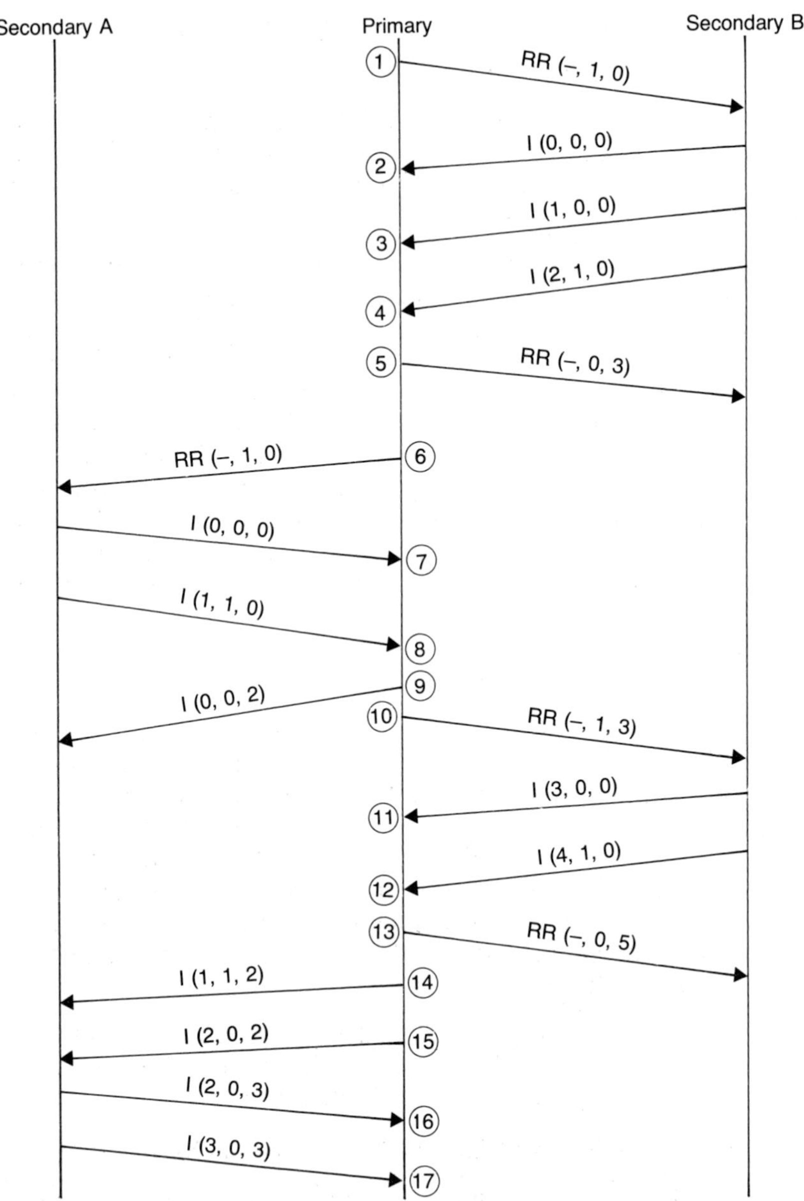

Figure 5.5 Tree Network Operation

16) I-frame, F-clear; acknowledges 0–2;

17) I-frame, F-clear.

In the example illustrated, the RR frames were all issued by the primary. If a secondary has no information to transfer to the primary it may also use the RR frame to acknowledge received I-frames.

Use of the RNR frame was introduced above. Its main purpose is to indicate an abnormal condition which is causing a terminal to suspend receipt of frames. A typical reason for this might be that the receiving terminal's buffer area is full. As such the RNR frame may be used during transmission of a window of frames before all of the frames have been received. This cancels any previous authority to transmit. The N(R) value of the RNR frame acknowledges receipt of all frames up to (and including) frame R–1 in the normal manner. Any frames received after R–1 will be discarded by the receiving terminal. Note that when in an RNR state a secondary may still receive and should act upon control or supervisory frames.

ADDRESSING

By using a single octet for addressing, a total of 256 separate addresses are theoretically available. If this is insufficient it is possible to use an extended addressing format. When using the extended addressing format the first transmitted bit of an address octet is set to '0' to indicate that the address continues in the following octet or is set to '1' to indicate that this is the final octet of the address. Hence the address field is unlimited although the use of two octets offers over 16,000 discrete addresses and three octets offers over 2 million.

The address 11111111 is called the 'global address' and is acted on by all stations. It may be used to poll stations whose address is unknown, such as may be found in dial-up links.

The address 00000000 is reserved as a 'no station' address and must not be assigned to any station. It may be used for testing purposes when frames are sent upon which no action is required.

A further addressing facility is the 'group address'. Any address may be allocated as a group address and several stations may act upon frames which carry such an address.

ERROR CONTROL

As in previous chapters, error control is discussed in terms of error detection and the error correction.

Error Detection

Two types of parity error detection were described in detail in Chapters 3 and 4 (VRC and LRC). Both of these depended on the information being structured into characters and are clearly not suitable for the bit-oriented HDLC procedures. An additional shortcoming of VRC/LRC was identified as being that error control was applied only to the user information segment of the message. Chapter 4 indicated that a further method of generating parity information was available, that of Cyclic Redundancy Checking (CRC). Note that although discussed in terms of its use for bit-oriented protocols, the technique of CRC is also applied to some variants of Basic Mode protocols in preference to the more common VRC/LRC system of parity information generation.

The basis of operation of CRC parity generating systems is to treat each transmission block as a single binary number. This number is divided by a fixed number to produce a quotient and a remainder. The remainder is then transmitted at the end of the data block as the parity information.

In practice the process is somewhat refined and practical systems make use of polynomial theory and modulo arithmetic. From this the technique of CRC is sometimes referred to as polynomial checking and the parity generating function is referred to as the polynomial function.

We shall now give an illustration of how this operates, using the simple polynomial $x^2 + 1$.

We shall assume that the message to be sent is:

1001001010

The polynomial representation of this is $x^9 + x^6 + x^3 + x^1$ and the binary equivalent of $x^2 + 1$ is 101.

The division in modulo 2 arithmetic is given in Figure 5.6. In practice the actual arithmetic at the transmitter and receiver is carried out by hardwired logic.

The complete block transmitted consists of the original data together with the remainder and is transmitted to line as follows:

original data	remainder
1 0 0 1 0 0 1 0 1 0	1 1

At the receiver, the calculation is performed on the incoming data and if no errors have occurred on the line, the received data should be exactly divisible by the generating polynomial as shown in Figure 5.7.

If the calculation at the receiver produces a remainder other than 0, this indicates that an error has been detected in the received data and the receiver requests a retransmission.

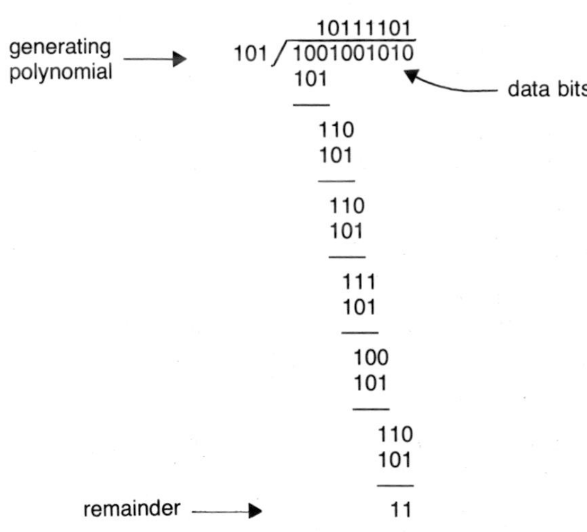

Figure 5.6 Generation of CRC Bits

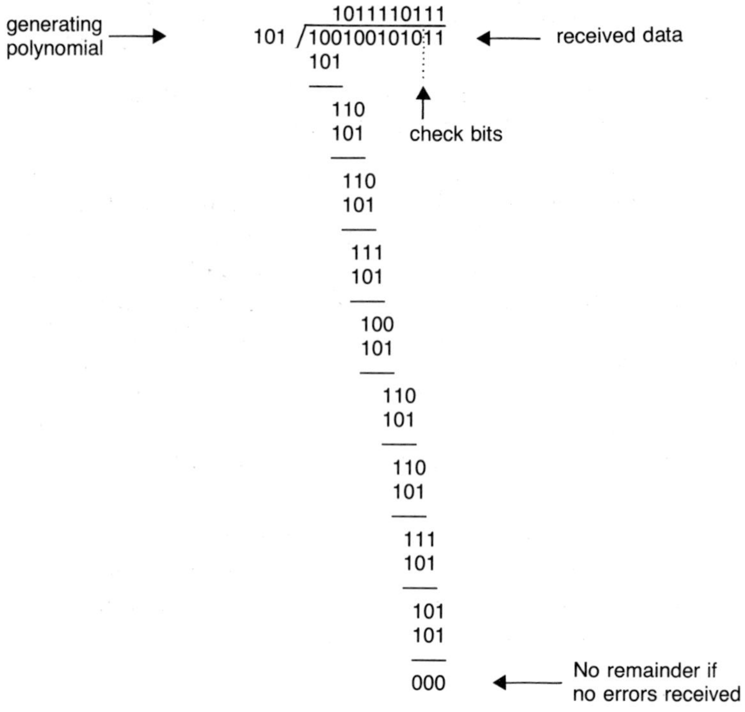

Figure 5.7 Division at the Receive Terminal of the Received Data by the Generating Polynomial

In practice the generating polynomial and algorithm which is actually used is that specified by CCITT Recommendation V.41. The polynomial is expressed symbolically as $x^{16} + x^{12} + x^5 + 1$. The precise details of the algorithm followed to determine the parity information (frame check sequence or FCS) demands division not only of the frame bit sequence but also of the number of bits contained in the frame. These two numbers are then summed (modulo 2) and the one's complement of the result forms the FCS. At the receiver the initial remainder is preset to all ones and the serial incoming protected data bits and the FCS, when divided by the generating polynomial, will result in a remainder of

$$x^{12} + x^{11} + x^{10} + x^8 + x^3 + x^2 + x^1 + 1 \text{ (ie 111010000111 1)}.$$

Note that for Basic Mode procedures a simpler algorithm which produces a remainder of zero is often used.

Through theoretical studies and subsequent practical experience this has been proved to be a very powerful error detection technique. For example, it has been found from computer simulation that when using a block size of 260 bits (including service bits and check bits) an improvement factor in the order of 50,000 is achieved. On a circuit with a mean error rate of 1 in 10^4 the residual error rate would, therefore, be in the order of 2 in 10^9, the 16 redundant bits comprising only 6.1% of each block. All odd numbers of errors within a block would be detected, also any one error burst not exceeding 16 bits in length and a large percentage of other error patterns.

It should be remembered that the additional bits inserted by the transparency mechanisms (bit stuffing) are not included in this check and also that the frame check sequence itself is subject to the transparency mechanism as described above.

Error Correction

We have already described the message-sequencing system for HDLC operation. The N(R) section of the C field allows acknowledgement of a number of frames, (ie N (R) = 5 acknowledges that all frames, from the last acknowledged frame up to frame 4, have been received successfully). If a frame is received and fails the CRC checking system, or has an incorrect sequence number, the receiving terminal will respond with a reject (REJ) frame. The N(R) number of this frame will be one more than the N(S) number of the last correctly received frame. The receiving terminal will discard the incorrectly received, and any subsequent, frames. The transmitting terminal must then retransmit the requested frame and all subsequent frames. This method of operation is known as the 'go back n' method.

Figure 5.8 illustrates the 'go back n' error recovery procedure. The sequence of frames is as follows:

1–4) I-frames, no errors;

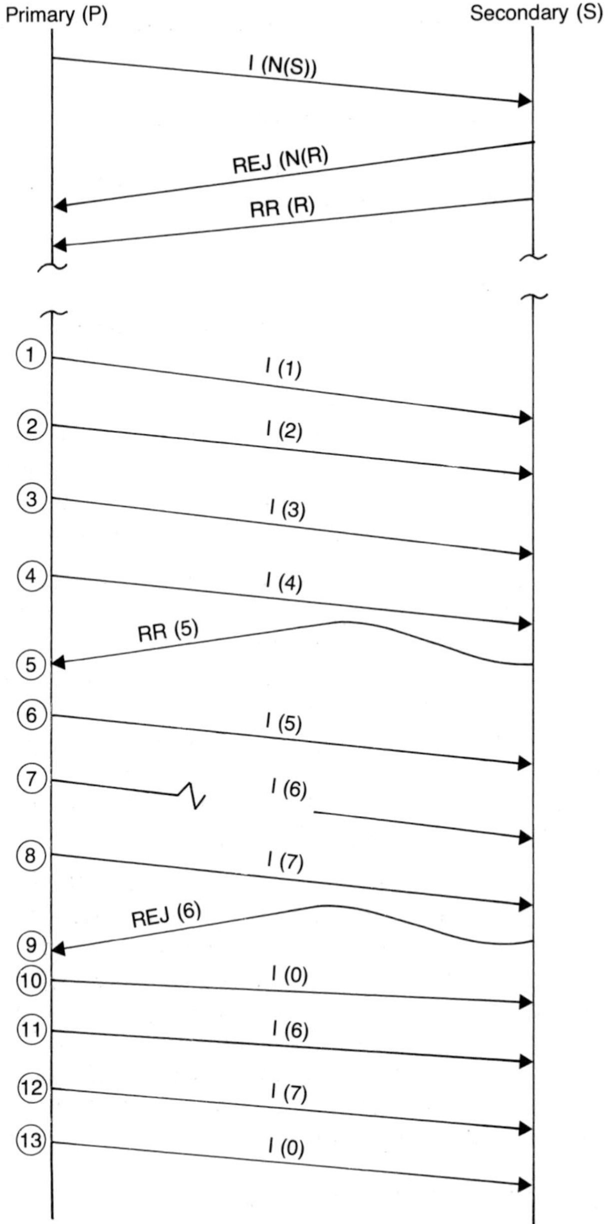

Figure 5.8 Error Handling – 'Go Back n' Method

5) RR acknowledges frames 1 to 4;

6) I-frame no error;

7) I-frame lost or received with errors;

8) I-frame no errors; but viewed by secondary as being out-of-sequence; the secondary must issue an REJ command;

9) REJ (6);

10) I-frame; although the primary has received the REJ command it has not yet processed it. Hence it continues with I (0)

11-13) I-frames. The primary has now processed the REJ frame and must retransmit the corrupted frame and all subsequent frames. The secondary must discard one copy of the duplicated frames (I (7) and I (0)).

It might appear that this method is rather inefficient as if the acknowledgements are lagging behind the transmitted sequence any error will cause the retransmission of several frames. This is not always a problem in that errors often occur in bursts such that if frame 'n' is corrupted then frame 'n + 1' may well also be corrupted. If however the extended numbering sequence option has been invoked an error in one frame could demand the retransmission of many frames unnecessarily. One technique of overcoming this is to use 'selective retransmission'.

Selective retransmission demands that only REJected frames need be retransmitted and the acknowledgement procedure for successfully received frames continues to operate as outlined above. This option utilises the SREJ (selective reject) frame. As the mnemonic implies this is used to request retransmission of a specific frame. Subsequent information frames which may have been received in the meantime are buffered. Hence the requirement for retransmission is limited to only those frames which were lost or corrupted during transmission.

MISCELLANEOUS FEATURES

During the course of this chapter several functions have been mentioned which were temporarily discarded without further information, in order to preserve the continuity of the descriptions being offered. In addition to this, several caveats have been given which referred to such generalisations as 'under normal operation'. This section attempts to clear up those outstanding issues in something of a random order providing a pot-pourri of information.

Two such commands are used to set 'extended response modes'. These are used to extend the length of the control field from one to two octets. This is required, for example, to support the increased N (S) and N (R) fields as described above. The commands are SNRME (Set Normal Response Mode Extended) and the SARME (Set Asynchronous Response Mode Extended). The revised format of the control field is given in Figure 5.9.

If a terminal is unable to comply with a command which it receives, the other party may be informed of this situation by means of the CMDR (Command Reject) response. Note that this frame may contain some diagnostic information in the I-field and as such is the only U-frame permitted to have a non empty I-field.

As the length of the I-field is unspecified and no mechanism exists by which a maximum length may be negotiated it is possible that a received I-type frame may be too long for the terminal to handle. Again this may be indicated by use of the CMDR facility.

A further facility is provided by the DISC (Disconnect) command. This is transmitted to indicate that no further transmission may take place until a new initialisation procedure has taken place. This command may be used for dial-up links to indicate that the circuit should then be physically disconnected and re-established.

OTHER FACILITIES

Various other actions are defined to complete the HDLC protocol specification:

- idle time between frames may be filled with consecutive flags;
- a frame may be aborted during transmission by transmitting at least seven consecutive ones (eg this may be required if the terminal sending the frame detects an error on retreiv-

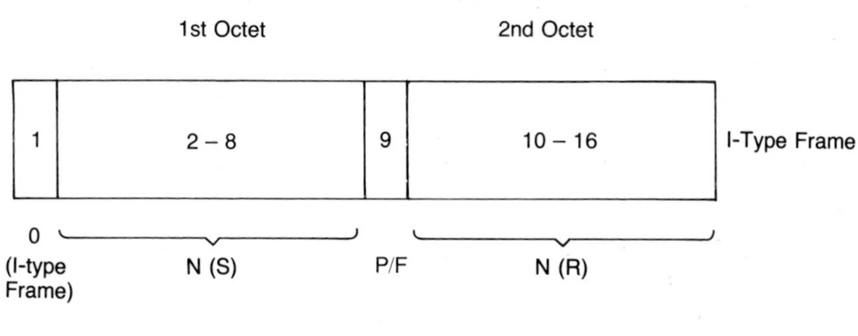

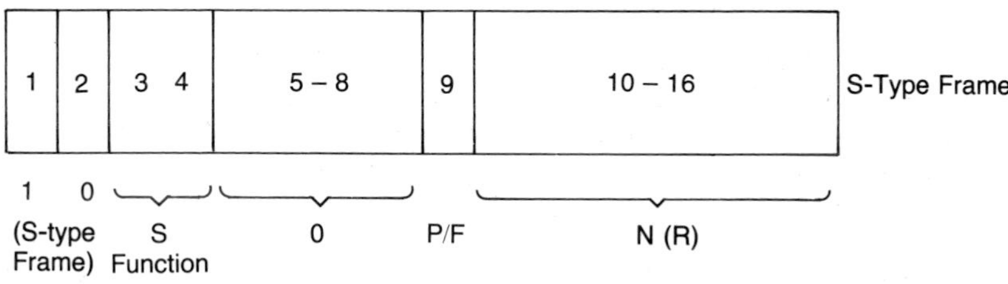

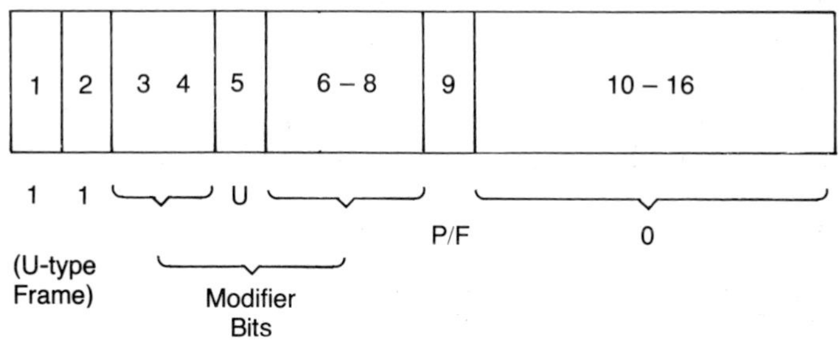

Figure 5.9 Extended Control Field

ing data from its own local memory). This can easily be interpreted as a breach of the transparency mechanism;

— a sequence of at least fifteen consecutive ones indicates that the sender is going inactive. This may be useful in a multi-drop configuration; or in a situation where the protocol is used with a half-duplex system requiring the sender to stop transmitting carrier and turn the modem round to receive the next incoming message. One configuration, in which the feature seems likely to gain popularity is when terminals are arranged in a local loop. A sequence of fifteen ones is then treated as a non-specific poll. As it progresses round the loop any device may insert a frame rather than forward the polling sequence and after sending the frame reverts to sending ones. Thus each terminal in turn can clear any messages which it has queued. Of course this may as a result impose heavy peak processing loads on the primary since it has no control over the propagation of the poll between the terminals on the loop. However on small loops this appears to be an attractive technique. Some manufacturers have implemented hub-polling systems on this basis for such applications as point-of-sale terminals within a single department or store.

SUMMARY OF FRAMES

In providing an overview of the method by which HDLC operates several commands and responses have been mentioned, both explicitly where their precise action was investigated and implicitly when particular functions were suggested. This summary begins with a list of the kernal of HDLC commands and responses.

I-type command; carries information, acknowledgements and polls;

I-type response; carries information and acknowledgements;

S-type (Commands or Responses);

RR (Receive Ready) provides flow control; carries acknowledgements;

REJ (Reject) used for ‘go back n’ error control;

RNR (Receive Not Ready) indicates inability to receive I-frames;

SREJ (Selective Reject) used for selective retransmission error control;

U-type Commands;

DISC (Disconnect) places secondaries in disconnected mode;

SARM (Set Asynchronous Response Mode) places secondary in ARM;

SARME (SARM Extended) places secondary in ARME;

SNRM (Set Normal Response Mode) places secondary in NRM;

SNRME (SNRM Extended) places secondary in NRME;

U-type responses;

CMDR (Command Reject) secondary cannot process frame; CMDR is only U-type which may have non-zero I-field (containing diagnostic information);

UA (Unnumbered Acknowledgement) acknowledges U-type command.

In addition to these commands there are also many optional features which may or may not be implemented on individual protocol variants. Even if implemented within the protocol their support by individual terminal systems may well be optional. This section provides a summary of these commands and responses. In general, but not always, these commands and responses will be used in the IM (Initialisation Mode).

Commands;

SIM (Set Initialisation Mode) initialises frames of secondary;

UI (Unnumbered Information) transmits information to secondary without updating N(S) or N(R);

UP (Unnumbered Poll) solicits current state of secondary;

XID (Exchange Identification) causes secondary to identify itself.

Responses;

DM (Disconnect Mode) reports secondary status as Disconnected requests mode-setting command from primary;

RD (Request Disconnect) asks primary to place secondary in DM;

RIM (Request Initialisation Mode) requests initialisation;

UI (Unnumbered Information) transmits information to primary without updating N(S) or N(R);

XID (Exchange Identification) response to XID command.

HDLC VIEWED AS A HIERARCHY

From an implementation viewpoint, HDLC may be viewed as a series of functional layers with a simple read/write interface between each level. Figure 5.10 illustrates this concept. The three layers are:

— the user level; this provides the address and the information portion of the frame;

— the scheduler level; this adds the link control field, covering such areas as ability to process further information frames;

— the transmission level; this is concerned with frame construction, error checking, interframe time fill and frame abortion.

The transmission level can also be regarded as a set of layers with a similar read/write interface convention.

The first transmission level computes and adds (or checks and removes) the frame check sequence. This is the layer which is permitted to abort a frame and is also responsible for interframe time fill, if it is required.

The second layer implants the bit stuffing/removing mechanism.

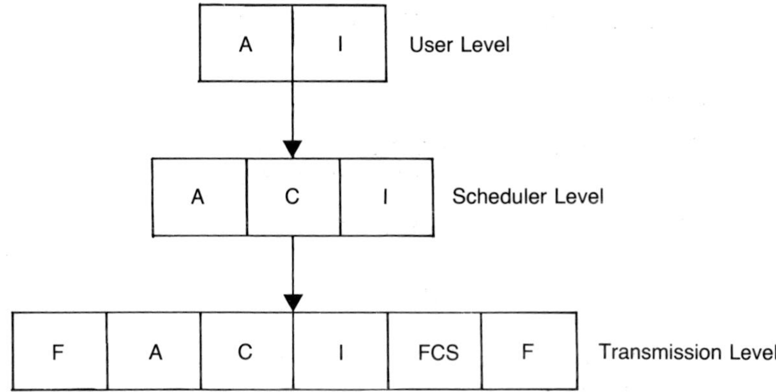

Figure 5.10 Layered Concept of HDLC

The third and layer surrounds the frame with the required flags.

This sub-layering is illustrated in Figure 5.11. It should be noted that this series of layers would normally be implemented in hardware.

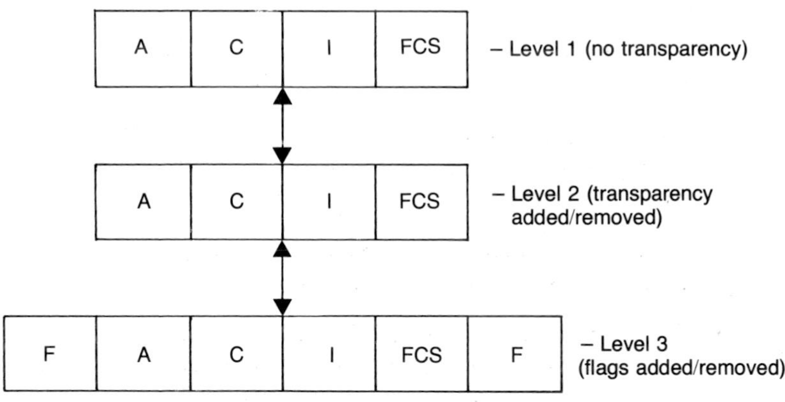

Figure 5.11 Sub-Layers of Transmission Level

RELATED STANDARDS AND PRODUCTS

At the same time as ISO were developing the HDLC procedures, other standards bodies were developing similar, but not identical, bit-oriented protocols. These included:

— Advanced Digital Communications Control Protocol (ADCCP) by the American National Standards Institute (ANSI);

— LAP (Level 2 of X.25) by CCITT.

Fortunately these and the other public standards do not differ by too much and in most cases have common sub-sets. Certainly the principles of operation are similar as indeed is much of the terminology.

Manufacturers have tended to align their bit-oriented protocols with one or more of these standards and as such a certain amount of interworking between proprietary versions is often possible. One of the beneficiaries of such alignment has of course been the producers of emulators and protocol convertors who can almost provide universal sub-sets of the full protocol.

The proprietary bit-oriented protocols include:

— BDLC (Burroughs);

— SDLC (IBM);

— UDLC (Univac).

Of course a supplier whose name is missing from this list is not necessarily to be scorned. Indeed on the contrary this may well indicate that the supplier supports one of the standard versions such as HDLC or ADDCP. The suppliers of the proprietary protocols listed may also support the standard or other proprietary versions.

INTERLUDE: BLOCK LENGTH

The aim of this publication is to provide the reader with not only an understanding of some specific protocols but also with the ability to comprehend the functions and structures of all protocols. One question worth considering is that of how long a message block should be. A number of factors which reflect the information given in the previous chapters of this book provide a basis for answering this question.

STRUCTURAL EFFICIENCY

This first point to consider is that a frame consists of two parts, system information and user information.

— system information consists of such fields as those used to carry addressing, error control and framing information. This part of the frame may be considered as an overhead;

— user information is, as far as the application is concerned, the useful part of the frame. It is the cargo of the message block.

In general, for any specific protocol, the system information of each message type will be of fixed length. The size of the information field will not substantially affect the size of the system information fields. Hence it would appear that a large frame equates to an efficient protocol.

ERROR HANDLING

If there is a large overhead in the block acknowledgement procedure (such as in Basic Mode operation), the time spent in the acknowledgement cycle will increase as block length decreases. Hence for a low error link, long block lengths are desirable.

If the distribution of errors is random the probability of an error occurring in any block (and hence that block being wasted) increases with block size. For this reason small block sizes are desirable. Furthermore, the amount of information to be retransmitted also increases with block size. These two factors are analogous to those experienced when deciding how often to take security dumps of computer programs. The overhead of taking a dump has to be balanced against the penalty of lost work if a failure occurs. An advanced solution to this problem is to have a block length which is dynamically altered to reflect the error frequency over a recent period. Although a good system to use in theory, it is seldom implemented.

EMULATION

When synchronous DLCPs were first developed it was convenient to make the new synchronous terminals look, to the host computer, as if they were existing peripherals. This meant that from the host's software viewpoint that the system was connected to known peripherals. This 'emulation' was clearly a major aid to the development of synchronous terminal software. It was therefore necessary to make the synchronous terminals transmit data in a format that was familiar to the mainframe such as card or paper tape 'image'. Hence information fields and thus block lengths were chosen to reflect the standard data field of the peripherals that were being emulated. This lead to blocks of data field length of either 80 characters (card image), 128 characters (paper tape image) or mutiples thereof.

MESSAGE HANDLING

There may be message lengths which can be conveniently handled by either mainframes or terminals. For instance when using a simple asynchronous TTY system each line of input (or output) may be treated as a message. As the operator keys in data it may be transferred to the host computer but no action is taken until the user sends a carriage return (CR) character. The central system will then process the line of data and respond accordingly. The structure of this message is then a number of characters followed by a CR.

PHYSICAL CONSTRAINTS

One of the more common forms of DLCP used for Bus-Topology Local Area Networks is CSMA/CD (Carrier Sense Multiple Access/Collision Detect). This system allows any terminal to begin transmission of a message provided that no other message is being transmitted at that time. If two nodes begin transmission at approximately the same instant there will be a 'collision' of information and both nodes can detect this. If two nodes were to transmit a very short block at the same time it would be possible that the blocks could collide after the nodes had stopped transmitting and hence not detect the collision. It is therefore necessary that blocks in this case have a minimum length.

The last example given above should remind the reader that many of the considerations made in this book apply not only to the 'traditional' data communications systems but to all communications systems whether traditional or new (or indeed to data or other forms of information).

6 Network Control Protocols

INTRODUCTION

The protocols described in the previous chapters provide sufficient facilities to allow strings of characters to be transferred between two DTEs which are connected by means of pre-existing data communications links. These links may in fact be part of complex networks with many terminal clusters and host systems but the protocols assume that there is a physical connection between the communicating devices. It is the final phrase of the above sentence which indicates the facility offered by Network Protocols. That is the means by which connections can be established through a network which does not maintain permanent paths between all communicating devices.

There are two ways in which the DTE may communicate with the network:

— direct communications: in this mode, messages are exchanged between the DTE and network control equipment without any significant alteration by the DCE (other than for a physical conversion say from V.24/V.28 to modulated carrier). An example of this mode of operation is layer 3 of X.25 (this is discussed in detail in later sections of this chapter);

— indirect communications: in this mode, network control messages are passed between the DTE and the DCE. The DCE then translates these commands to the format demanded by the network, performing a 'protocol conversion' function. An example of this mode of operation is that of the use of Automatic Call equipment and CCITT V.25

procedures. Again these will be discussed in more detail below.

We have stated that the requirement being discussed here is that of the exchange of information between the information processing devices and the communications network itself. The types of information which may be exchanged include:

- addressing – ie where devices are located;
- routeing – ie how to get there;
- service levels – such as priority or security of transfer;
- charging/accounting information.

Not every network layer protocol will support every one of the facilities listed above. For example, an address may be required (at least at call set-up time) but the route may be determined solely by the network itself.

ADDRESSING

There are two basic methods of constructing addresses of network entities: *flat* and *hierarchical* addressing schemes.

The value of an individual 'flat' address is allocated from a universal set of address values and need not reflect the topology of the network or the physical location of the entity to which that value is allocated. An example of a flat addressing scheme is that of the telephone extension numbers of a Stored-Program Control PABX (SPC PABX). It is always necessary to provide a mechanism by which the route to the destination can be determined from that address. Where flat addressing is employed this is usually achieved in the form of a routeing table.

The value of any individual 'hierarchical' address is dependent upon the location of the entity to which it applies.

This form of address is structured in such a way as to reflect the topology of the host network(s) and therefore can assist in the operation of message routeing mechanisms by providing directly information concerning the route along which the message should proceed. An example of a hierarchical addressing scheme is that employed in the Public Switched Telephone Network.

ROUTEING

There are three common techniques for network routeing systems. These are circuit switching, message switching and packet switching.

Circuit Switching

In a circuit switched system the end-to-end connection between the information processing terminals is established before information transfer begins and remains established until the communications session is completed. The application of circuit switching with which people are most familiar is that used in the public telephone system.

The three phases of a circuit switched communications session are:

Call establishment:	a physical association between the communicating parties is established.
Information transfer:	the physical connection established above is maintained during this phase.
Call release:	the physical connection between the two parties is terminated and the associated equipment released.

This chapter is concerned chiefly with the first and third stages of this procedure. However there may also be exchanges of information between the network control equipment and the information processing equipment during the information transfer phase of a call.

Use of the PSTN for circuit switched data communications illustrates another important aspect of the network protocols. That is that the lower functions such as error control can act independently to the network control or topology, or indeed any other higher functions. Consider the simple terminal point-to-point link shown in Figure 6.1. If we replace the direct data communications link by a telephone circuit and establish the circuit (either manually or by some automatic device) before data transmission takes

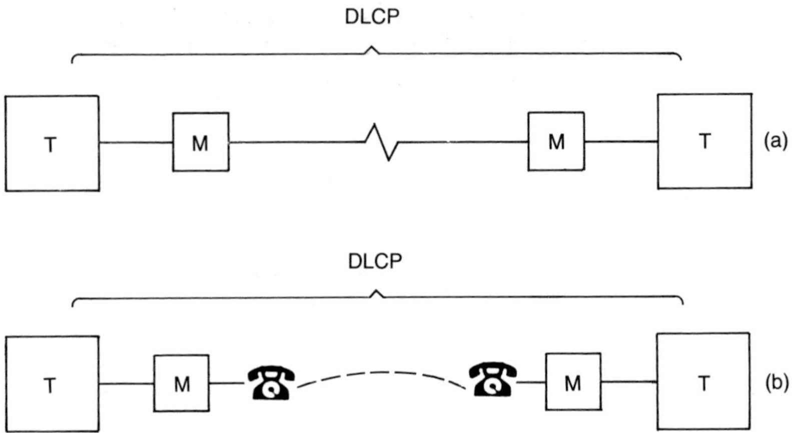

Figure 6.1 Use of Switched Circuit for Data Transmission

place we can still transfer information as before using a simple DLC protocol.

Circuit switched systems offer network control in 3 ways:

— manual operation;

— discrete automatic control;

— integrated automatic control.

Manual operation is used where each call is set up by a human operator. The most common example in the field of data communications is that of a modem used over the PSTN. Here an operator may establish a telephone connection between the two terminals before switching to data transfer mode. Such a system is illustrated in Figure 6.1.

Discrete automatic control provides an automatic version of the above, where the network control information is passed over a physical interface which is separate from the physical interface used for end-to-end information transfer. An example of this method is found in the use of Automatic Calling Equipment

(ACE), modems and the PSTN. Such a configuration is shown in Figure 6.2. Note that the call control terminal may be independent of the information processing terminal.

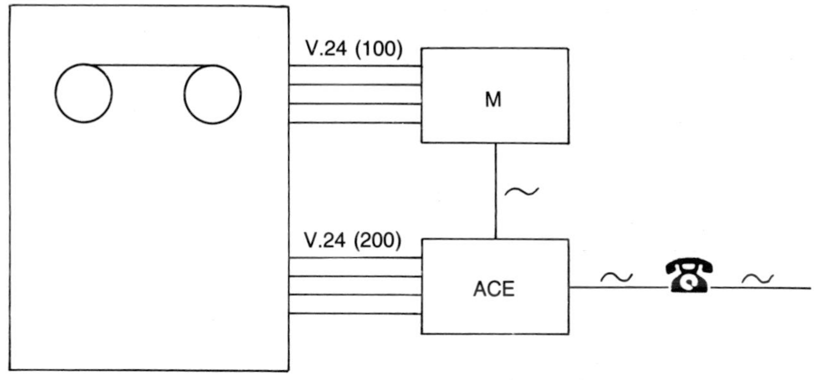

Figure 6.2 ACE Configuration

The procedure for controlling a call complies with CCITT Recommendation V.25. (using the 200 series V.24 interchange circuits). Figure 6.3 presents a summary of the procedure for establishing a connection. The procedure is also summarised below with the manual call analogy given in parenthesis. Note that the numbers shown (2 X X) refer to the 200 series functions.

1) The call control terminal indicates a call request (lift handset off cradle);
2) This is authorised by the network (hear dialling tone);
3) The address digits are given to the network (dialling);
4) The remote terminal answers (called party answers);
5) A tone is sent to inform distant terminal that call has originated from an automatic system (caller says 'hello').

V.25 also specifies the appropriate procedures for automatic answering of calls.

Integrated automatic call control provides the third and probably most advanced form of call control. Under this configuration

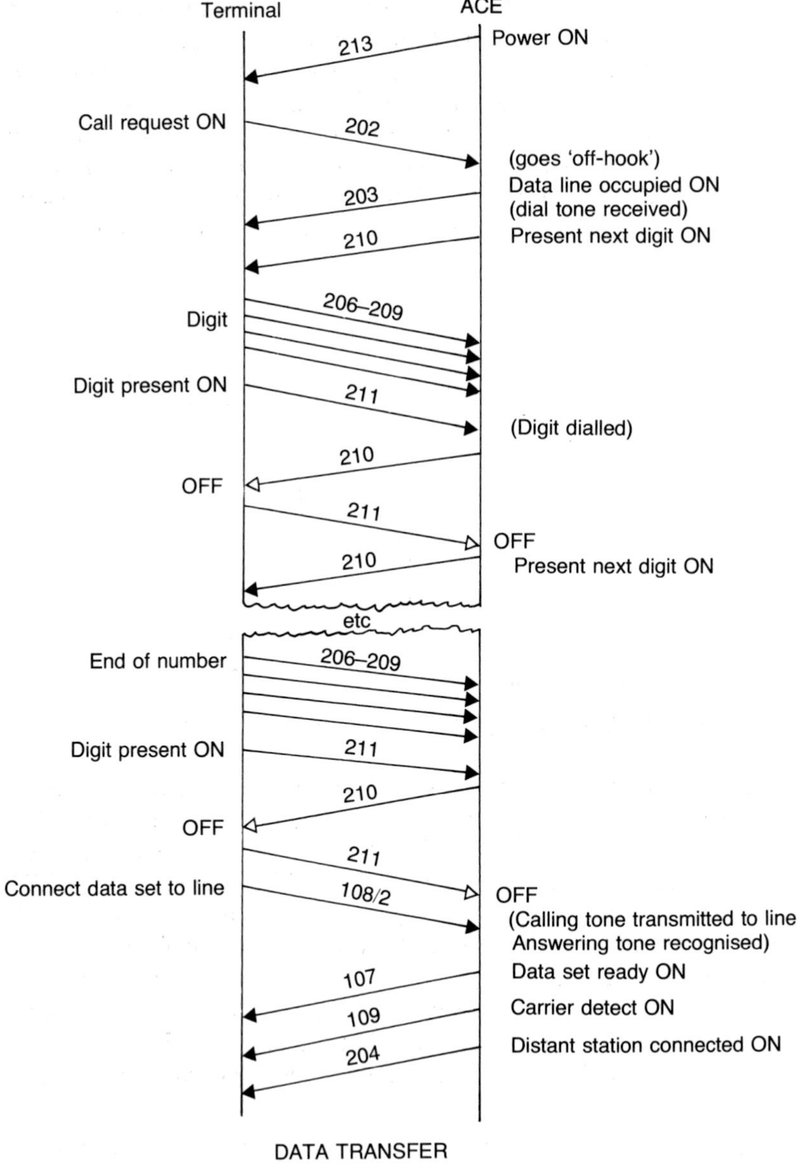

Figure 6.3 V.25 Call Set-Up Procedure

the network-control and user information are transferred across the same interface. One method of achieving this is becoming increasingly popular for use with microcomputer terminals, and modems capable of performing PSTN control by this method are now available. The configuration of such a system is shown in Figure 6.4. The call-initialisation takes place under control of the DTE and after the call is established normal link-level data transfer takes place. The DTE may also terminate the link by control of the DTE/DCE interface.

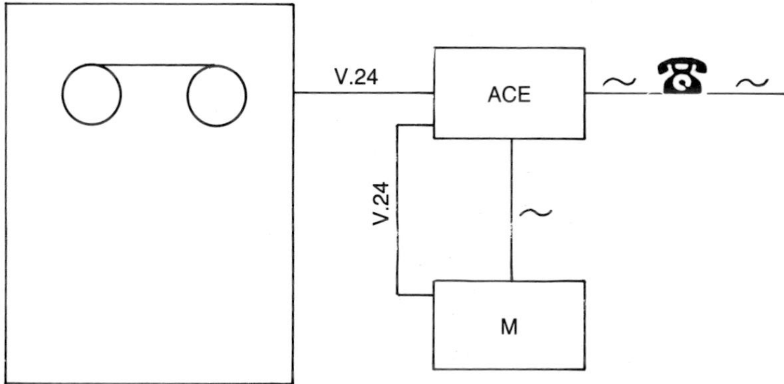

Figure 6.4 Integrated Automatic Call Control

Another example of an 'integrated' network control protocol is that of CCITT Recommendation X.21. X.21 is often considered to be just a Physical Level Protocol. In fact this is not true. Rather like CCITT Recommendation X.25 (discussed in detail below), X.21 covers, or perhaps more accurately involves, data-link and network layers in addition to the physical functions. The physical elements of X.21 include the electrical (X.26/X.27), functional (X.24) and mechanical (ISO DIS 4903) characteristics. However X.21 also includes procedures for operation over circuit switched data networks which involve both the data-link and network layer elements.

At the network level X.21 provides a control mechanism for the three phases of a call:

— call set-up;

— user-information transfer;

— call clear.

Figure 6.5 summarises the X.25 network control procedure. The function of most of the commands should be clear to the reader and hence the description below restricts itself to those elements whose purpose might not be so obvious. This figure identifies five sub-sets of the dialogue:

— calling-terminal call set-up: the selection signals consist of two elements – the requests for levels of service (or optional features) and the destination address. The DCE waiting signal is really misnamed. It is an optional signal which is used to indicate that a call attempt has failed (it is shown broken as in this scenario it would not be used);

— called-terminal call set-up: the call information is an optional function which may provide such information as the address of the call originator or charging information;

— the user-information exchange phase: this requires little comment except that the request to terminate this phase may be made by either party;

— clearing-terminal call clear: the clearing procedure consists of a simple request-confirmation pair. After the call has been cleared the DTE should return to the 'ready' (for further calls) state;

— cleared-terminal call clear: again a simple request-confirmation pair is used.

X.21 provides a highly sophisticated set of functions at the network layer and the overview given above should be seen only as an introduction. Other facilities which may be implemented at the network level are:

— abbreviated addressing;

— called line identification;

— calling line identification;

— charge advice;

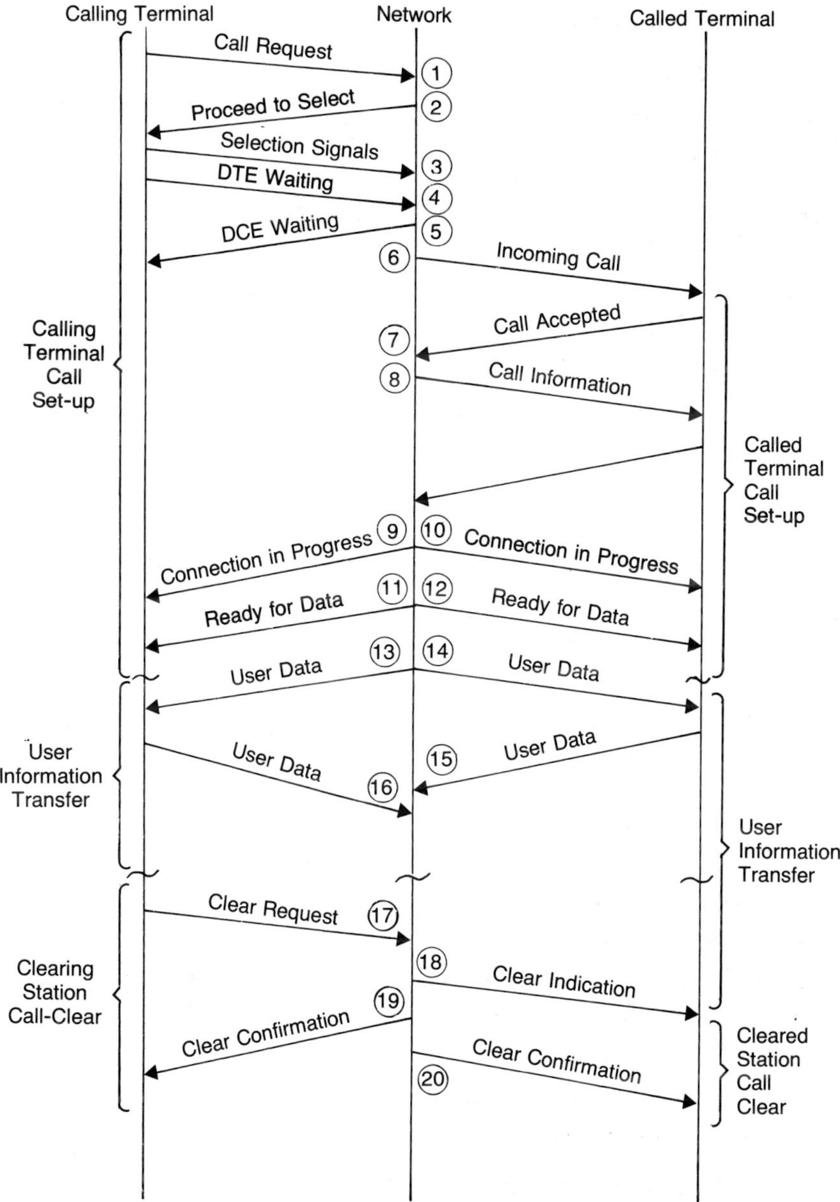

Figure 6.5 X.21 Network Control

- closed user group;
- direct call;
- facility registration/cancellation;
- fast call select;
- incoming call redirection;
- multiple addressing.

As no public circuit-switched data network is currently provided in the UK, the use of X.21 at the network level is often not an option to the UK computer user. (Although public circuit-switched networks are available in many other countries.) The introduction of public access to BT's ISDN (Integrated Services Digital Network) in the form of the IDA (Integrated Digital Access) may result in the provision of some X.21 based network control facilities in the future and hence this is a protocol to be dismissed at the reader's peril.

The reasons for choosing (or not) to use circuit switching are many and varied. High on the list might be that it is the only automatic option available. However if any choice is offered it is often wise to consider its merits and demerits.

There are several advantages to circuit switching:

- it is simple to operate, either by a manual process such as in a telephone call or by automatic equipment such as an auto-call device;
- the destination address is transferred only during the call set up stage and need not be repeated during the information transfer session;
- all aspects of the network routeing process are carried out in isolation from the actual data link session. This means that after the call has been set up a data link protocol may be used as if the connection were permanent;
- it may be the only option either available as a public service or supported by a DCE supplier.

The disdvantages of circuit switching are that:

— although the data link control protocol may be able to support a complex tree network the circuit switched network will not normally provide anything beyond a point-to-point connection;

— the network circuit is dedicated to the connection for the duration of the session. As there is often no method of interrupting the session allocation of resources is restricted;

— in many cases the network will be transferring user information for only a small percentage of the connection time, but the charge made to the user for use of the service will be based on connection time.

These advantages and disadvantages serve to indicate the types of applications which are well suited to circuit switching circuits. These applications have the following characteristics:

— long connect time;

— few changes of network connection;

— high volume or busy connections.

Examples which fall into these catagories are file transfer systems and on-line systems requiring a single connection between multi station terminal systems. Note that the facilities of the data oriented circuit-switched networks overcome many of these problems and extend the range of useful applications to cover short-duration interactive use.

Message Switching

Message switching systems relay entire messages between adjacent network nodes before forwarding the entire message to the next node. If a message is to be sent between A and C via B the complete message, together with addressing and possibly control information, will be transferred between A and B and stored in B. Only after this has been achieved will the message be forwarded to the next node point, which in this case is the destination node C. This technique is often called store and forward. Message switching systems do not operate in real-time mode as there can be considerable delay between the transmission of a message and its reception. Although this technique is often used in text transmission systems its extended (and unpredictable) transmission time has severely restricted its application to computer data transfer systems. It is not discussed in any detail in this book.

Packet Switching

Although the initial concept of packet switching systems was intended as a method of providing a secure method of transmitting speech in a military environment, their potential for use in data communications systems was recognised and this is now their primary environment. They provide a data-oriented version of public telephony networks, combining some of the characteristics of circuit switched and message switched systems. In fact their use for data communications is now sufficiently important to justify that the rest of this chapter is devoted to their general description followed by a detailed section concerning the CCITT Recommendation (X.25) around which most of the systems are based.

The principle of packet switching is to segment the information to be transferred into a number of message blocks (or packets) of restricted length. Each packet is then transmitted as a separate message to the recipient. In a complex network the packets of a single message may utilise differing routes through the network although the final network node must ensure that they are delivered to the recipient DTE in their correct sequence. This highlights again, one of the important aspects of network control protocols – they are concerned with the communication between the DTE and its serving network control equipment. They are not concerned with the method by which the network transports information (including that of the user) from end to end. This variable routeing of individual packets means that there is no permanent dedicated connection between the originator and the recipient even during a communications session. Because of this the physical association between the originator and the recipient is known as a virtual circuit. This is illustrated in Figure 6.6.

As each message is segmented into packets it is possible to interleave packets such that a single terminal interface may support a number of virtual circuits concurrently. In this way the

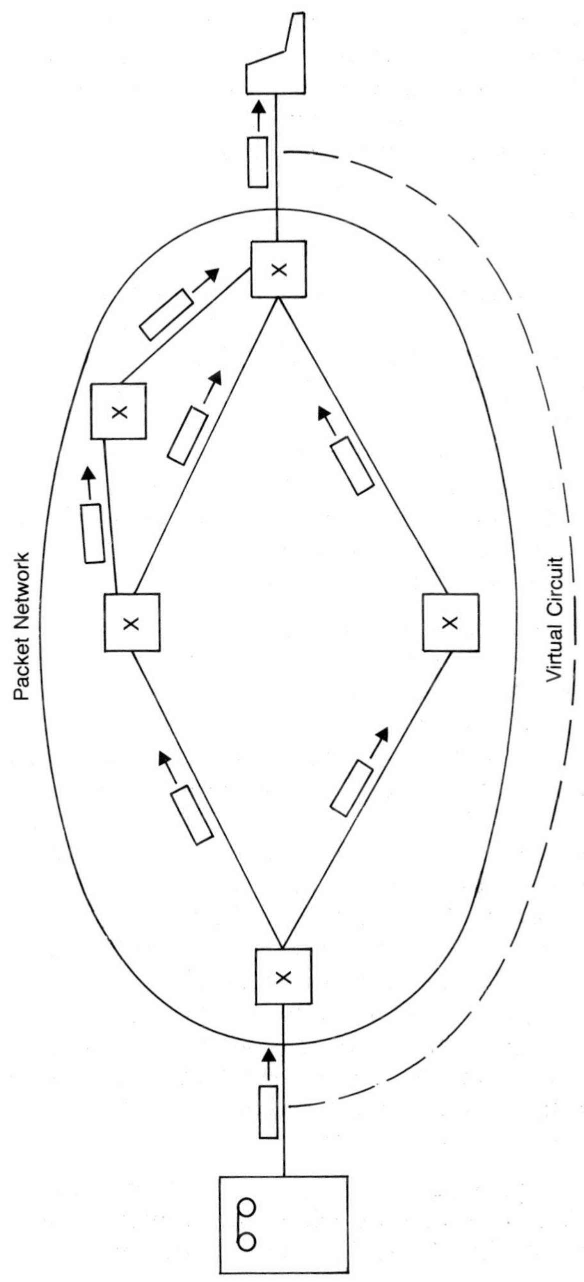

Figure 6.6 Virtual Circuits

connection between the DTE and the local Packet Switching Exchange (PSE) may be considered to be divided into a number of channels. As these channels are not of fixed order or usage they are referred to as 'logical channels'. This is illustrated in Figure 6.7a. As a logical channel occupies the line between the DTE and the PSE only when it is transferring information the effect of the logical channel concept may be seen as that of a statistical multiplexer. Each virtual circuit occupies one logical channel between the originating DTE and the local PSE. Similarly the same virtual circuit occupies a logical channel between the recipient DTE and its local PSE. Virtual channels are purely local entities, allocated to virtual calls on a local basis (see Figure 6.7b). Because of this the number allocated to a virtual circuit will generally be different at each end, ie logical channel 2 at originating node and logical channel 6 at the answering node. Figure 6.8 shows the association between logical channels and virtual circuits.

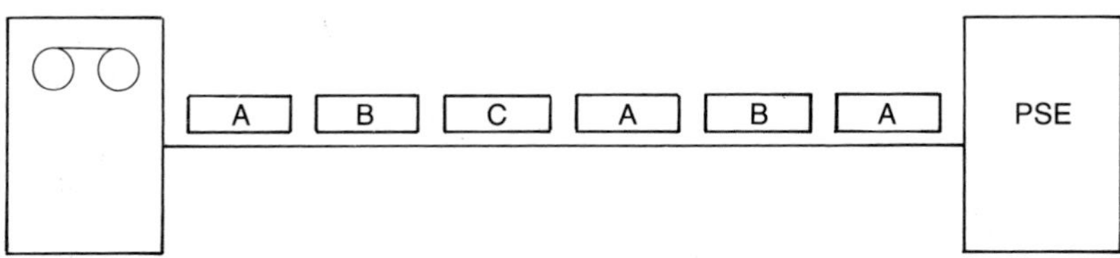

Figure 6.7a Logical Channels

Packet switched networks operate in real time demanding that any store-and-forward operation of network nodes must be of short duration. As with other protocols there are three phases to information transfer:

- call initialisation;
- data transfer;
- call termination.

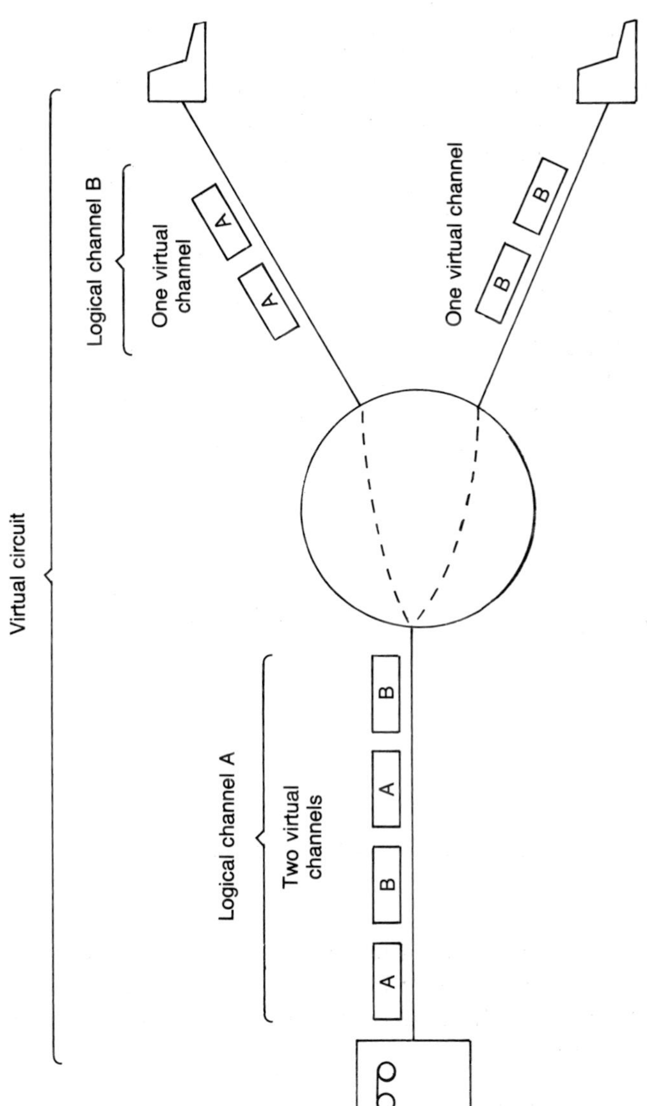

Figure 6.7b Virtual Circuits and Virtual Channels

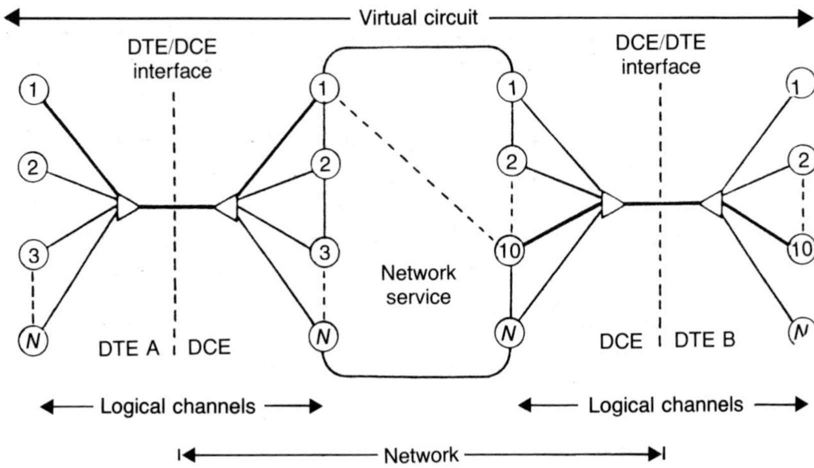

Figure 6.8 Virtual Circuits and Logical Channels

Call initialisation consists of several distinct steps:

— reserve a logical channel between the originating DTE and its local PSE;

— inform the local PSE of the recipient's address;

— reserve a logical channel between the recipient's PSE and DTE;

— ensure that the recipient is ready and able to accept the information to be transferred.

As with other protocols there are two types of information to be transferred: user data and control data. The information transfer phase consists of sending a sequence of packets from the originating DTE to its PSE. These are transferred through the network and may arrive at the recipient's local PSE in a random order. They are then ordered at the PSE before being transferred to the recipient in their correct sequence, possibly interspersed by packets from other virtual circuits.

Note: having established the connection between the local logical channel and the logical circuit, each packet need only contain the logical channel number to inform the local PSE of the destination of that packet.

The call termination phase consists of terminating the virtual circuit and releasing the logical channels between each DTE and its PSE.

Full details of the procedures outlined above are given in the sections to follow. There are in practice two types of virtual circuits. These are the Switched Virtual Circuit (SVC) and the Permanent Virtual Circuit (PVC). It is the SVC which operates in the manner described above and has the following characteristics:

— it exists only for the duration of one network session;

— available logical channels may be used consecutively for many virtual circuits;

— SVCs require a call set up procedure;

— as its name suggests the PVC is merely a VC that is maintained during inter-session gaps (ie on a permanent basis);

— it has permanently allocated logical channels which cannot be used for other VCs;

— no call set up is required (at the network layer).

It is the last characteristic of the SVC and PVC which determines that for the remainder of this chapter (where X.25 is detailed) the emphasis will be placed upon the use of SVCs.

The concept of the SVC as described above is suitable for messages which extend over many packets. Provision is also made in X.25 for the special case of messages which can be contained in a single packet. These facilities, known as Datagrams and Fast Call Select options are described in detail below.

SERVICE LEVELS

Under some protocols, provision is made to allow the DTE to request certain levels of service from the network. These will fall into one of two groups of functions:

— quality of service: this includes such features as speed of delivery (in a store-and-forward system) or security of information.

— value-added facilities: these include such services as abbreviated addressing, closed user groups, protocol conversion or information concerning the cost of the session.

CCITT RECOMMENDATION X.25

The terms 'packet switching' and 'X.25' are in danger of becoming synonymous. This practice is rather perilous and if there is any doubt about which is being referred to, clarification of actual intent should always be sought. Packet switching is a technique of telecommunications described above. X.25 is a recommendation which defines the interface between a packet-mode data terminal and a public data network ie the Packet Switching Exchange (PSE). X.25 is not concerned with the internal operation of the network itself, the only constraint being that packets belonging to a virtual call are delivered from the network in the same sequence that they are entered into it.

The recommendation itself covers three levels corresponding to the protocol levels discussed in this book. These levels are:

Level 1: the physical interface which specifies the interface between the DTE and DCE.

Level 2: the link-access protocol which is intended to provide error-free transportation of packets over the error-prone DTE to PSE circuit. Level 2 utilises the HDLC protocol as described in Chapter 5.

Level 3: the packet level. This is the network protocol.

Figure 6.9 shows the layered structure of X.25

Level 1: The Physical Interface

As stated above, level 1 is concerned with the physical and electrical properties of the interface presented to the subscriber at the network circuit termination. The original intention of CCITT was that this should be identical to the X.21 physical level recommendation but this proved to be unacceptable due to the large user-base of V.24/V.28 terminals. As a result of this the operation of the physical level interface to X.21 bis (V.24/V.28 compatible) is also permitted.

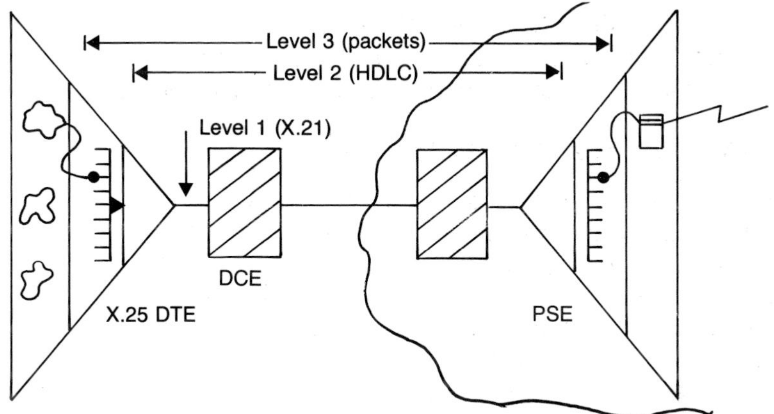

Figure 6.9 Layered Structure of X.25

Level 2: The Link Access Protocol

Two link-level protocols have been defined under X.25. These are:

— Link Access Protocol (LAP);

— Link Access Protocol Balanced (LAPB).

The original DLCP, LAP is based on the Asynchronous Response Mode (ARM) of HDLC (ie unbalanced operation). A second DLCP (LAPB) was specified which provides for operation under the Asynchronous Balanced Mode (ABM) of HDLC. In practice many networks provide access in either mode. Details of HDLC are given in Chapter 5.

The level 3 packet of X.25 is carried in the information field of the level 2 packet as shown in Figure 6.10.

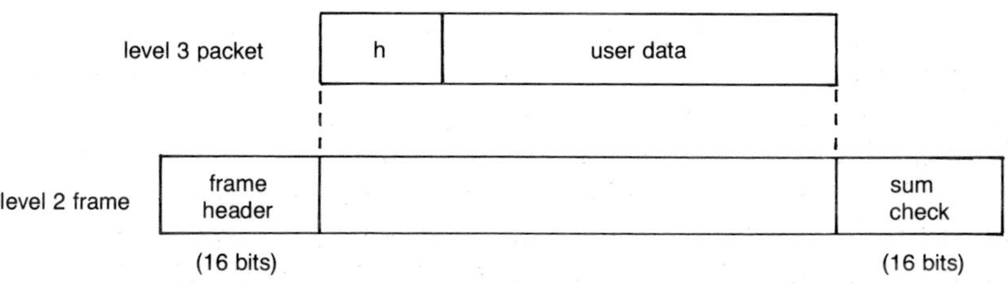

Figure 6.10 Transportation of Level 3 Packets

Level 3: The Network (or Packet) Level.

As this chapter is concerned with network control protocols it will not be a surprise to find that the remainder of the chapter will focus on level 3 of X.25. In particular, emphasis will be placed on the network procedures for SVCs.

PACKET FORMAT

Level 3 packets consist of two sections, 'header' and 'information'. There are several different formats and types of packet which will be discussed in detail below. All headers consist of:

— a general format identifier;

— logical channel identifier;

— one or more other fields.

Figure 6.11 illustrates the general format of an X.25 packet.

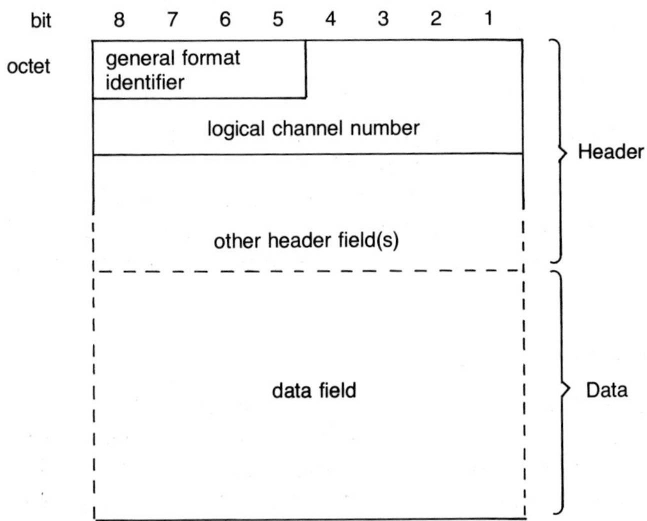

Figure 6.11 X.25 Level 3 Packet Format

General Format Identifier

This occupies bits 5–8 of the first octet. It is used to indicate the format of the packet. Different formats are used for each of the following groups of packet:

— call set-up;

— control packets;

— data packets;

— datagram packets;

— fast select packets.

Where appropriate different packet formats for a particular packet type are required to reflect the window size of the packet sequencing scheme (modulo 8 and modulo 128 are available).

This field may also contain other information carried via the D-bit (bit 7) or the Q-bit (bit 8 of data packets).

Details of the specific value of the general format identifier for each packet type and the use of the D and Q bits are given in the text to follow.

Logical Channel Identifier

This is made up of a logical channel group number (bits 1 to 4 of octet 1) and a logical channel number (all bits of octet 2). This provides 15 groups of 256 channels, ie a possible total of 2,688 logical channels. In practice a subset of these channels which may be used will be agreed between the network administration and the user.

Other Fields

All packets contain a header of at least 3 octets and one or more fields are always present in addition to the general format identifier and logical channel identifier fields. These additional fields, discussed in detail below, serve the following purposes:

— packet type indication; used to identify the specific packet type where one general format is shared between several packet types;

— sequencing information; used to indicate the sequence number of the packet, or the sequence number of the next expected received packet;

— address fields; used to carry information concerning the address of the packet origin and/or destination;

— facility fields; used to carry information concerning requests for optional facilities;

— supervisory field; used to indicate reason for supervisory or control packets (such as reset cause, etc);

— user data.

This chapter continues by considering the various functions which the packets must carry out and examines the structure of each packet in turn.

The three stages of a communications session (set-up, data transfer and termination) are described and then exception conditions and procedures not already listed are described.

Finally this section takes a look at some of the optional services described in X.25.

CALL CONTROL

Call Set-up

In order to set up a virtual call, the calling DTE sends a 'call request' packet to the local PSE. The information contained in the packet is passed through the network and an 'incoming call' packet is delivered to the called DTE. This has the same structure as the call request packet and contains complementary information. Figure 6.12 illustrates the format of these packets.

The general format identifier is coded as follows:

0 D 0 1 (modulo 8)

0 D 1 0 (modulo 128)

Two sequence numbering schemes are available under X.25. Although both schemes have the same call request/incoming call packet structure the information contained in here determines the

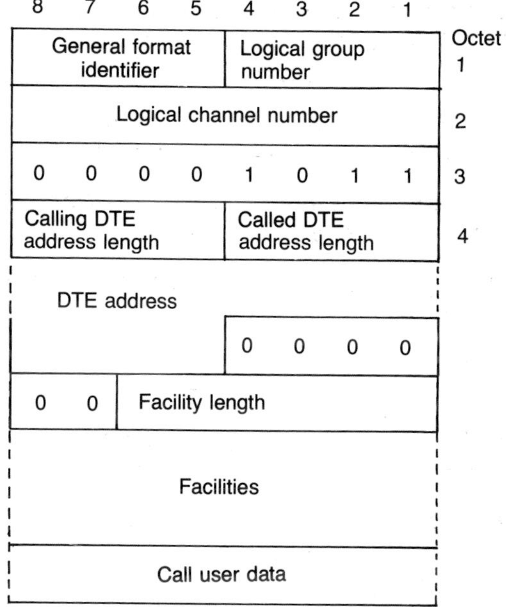

Figure 6.12 Call Request/Incoming Call Packet Format

mode of operation and hence format of the packets to follow in the session.

Packet acknowledgement uses a sliding window technique as described for HDLC. The D-bit is used in data packets to solicit immediate confirmation of packet receipt, rather than waiting until the window is full. In the call set up routine the D-bit may be set in a call request packet to determine whether the receiver can support this (optional) feature. The response to this enquiry is given by the state of the D-bit in the call accept packet (see below).

Logical Channel Number

The logical channel number of an SVC is allocated at the time of call set-up. The call originating DTE selects a logical channel number for the path between itself and the associated PSE. At the call receiving end, the logical channel number is selected by the PSE.

Each logical channel is dedicated to one of three uses:

— SVC;

— PVC;

— Datagram.

The use of a logical channel may not be altered during normal operation and hence if PVCs or datagrams are used not all idle logical channels may be available for new SVCs.

In order to provide a well defined calling regime an algorithm for available channel selection is given in X.25. At the DTE the highest available channel number is selected for an outgoing call. The network, on the other hand, always selects the lowest available channel number for an incoming call. Thus collision (both DTE and PSE bidding for the same logical channel) will only occur when a single channel is left available. If this does occur then the PSE will automatically reject the call request and preference will be given to the incoming call. Note that this conflicts with the X.21 collision procedure in which the DTE is given preference.

The PSE at each end of the virtual circuit will retain the association of the logical channel number and the remote terminal address. Hence it is not necessary to include explicitly the address of the remote DTE in any packet after the call set-up phase, the logical channel number providing implicit addressing information.

Address Fields

There are two 'address length' fields and one 'address value' field. Provision is made to allow variable length addressing to be used, the length of each address being given by the calling DTE (in the calling DTE address and called DTE address length fields). The requirement for variable length addressing is as follows:

— different networks may have different addressing schemes. Hence the basic address length of two different DTEs may be of different lengths;

— a network may allow 'short code' addressing of local connections to be made. This is analagous to the dialling of a local telephone number without including the STD code;

— a facility known as abbreviated addressing may be offered by the network. This allows a terminal to enter a short code to represent the full address of a regularly called number. In this case the network itself must map an abbreviated address, supplied by the DTE, to the full remote address.

By the methods described above, the address of a single called DTE may be specified to the network in up to three ways, full address, short code address and abbreviated address.

It should also be noted that the inclusion of the calling DTE address may be optional and will therefore not always be found in a call address/incoming call packet.

Facilities Field

Many optional facilities are specified in X.25. The caller may request either no facilities in which case the facilities length field = 0, or one or more facilities in which case the facilities length field ≠ 0.

User Data

Finally, a user data field is provided which may contain up to 16 octets of information. A typical use of this field is to carry password or log-on information. This field may be used wholly for data or a portion of it may be used to carry protocol information to the network. This distinction is indicated by the content of bits 8 and 7 of the first user-data octet. A special extension to this field is provided under the fast-select facility.

Call Acceptance

Call acceptance is indicated by the issue of a 'call accept' packet from the called terminal. This is delivered to the calling terminal as a 'call confirmation' packet. Again these packets are complementary to each other.

Figure 6.13 shows the structure of a call accept or call confirmation packet. Note that this is similar to the call request/incoming call packet but no data field is available. Again a special packet is available for use with the fast-select feature.

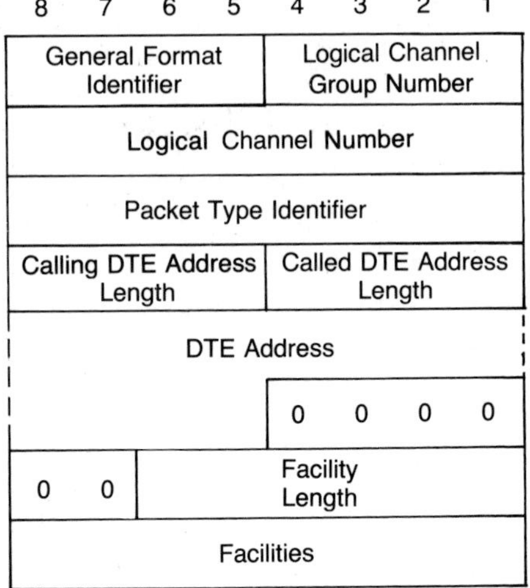

Figure 6.13 Structure of Call Accept/Call Confirmation Packet

The general format identifier of the packet is coded as follows:

0 D 0 1 for modulo 8 operation

0 D 1 0 for modulo 128 operation

The functions of the D-bit and remaining fields are as described above for the call set-up packets.

It is of course possible that the call request may not be accepted by the called DTE, or the original call request may be invalid and hence refused by the network. In the first case the called party returns a 'call clear request' packet in response to the incoming call. In both cases the network issues a 'call clear indication' packet to the calling DTE, containing information about why the call request was refused. Details of these packets are given in the section below which considers call termination.

Information Transfer

Once a virtual call is established either subscriber may send and should expect to receive 'data' packets. The structure of these packets is given in Figure 6.14.

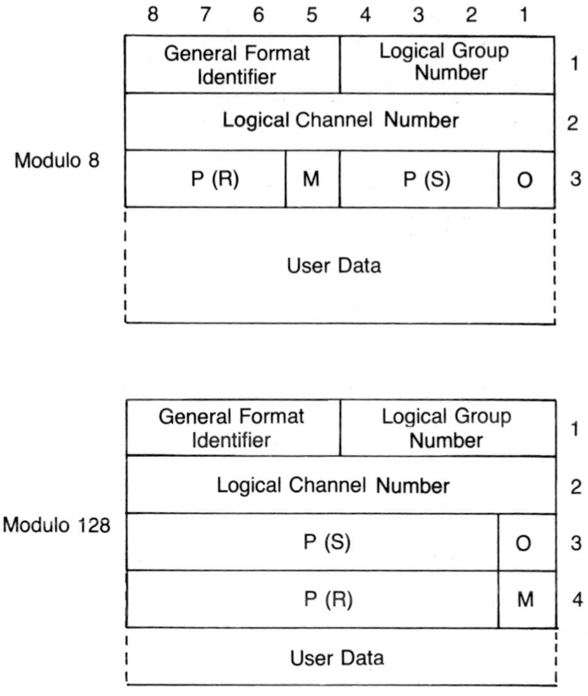

Figure 6.14 Structure of Data Packets

The structure and purpose of the fields within data packets are as follows:

General Format Identifier:

Q D 0 1 for modulo 8 operation

Q D 1 0 for modulo 128 operation

The Q-bit provides a mechanism by which the user system may operate two streams (or levels) of data across a single virtual circuit. If this facility is not used, the default value for the Q-bit is specified to be 0. If the facility is used data packets may contain data at 'level 0' or 'level 1'. It is not possible to mix data levels within a single packet. Additionally each 'data sequence' (see below) must consist of data at a single level.

One use of the Q-bit concerns the exchange of information between an X.25 DTE and a remote terminal concentrator (known as a packet assembly/disassembly device or PAD). It is necessary to be able to distinguish between control messages to and from the PAD and user data to and from the simple terminal using the PAD. The Q-bit is set to '1' for PAD messages, the description of which can be found in CCITT Recommendation X.29. Packets destined for the terminal, or assembled by the PAD from a terminal, have the Q-bit set to '0'.

Packet Sequencing

Two fields are provided in a data packet for packet sequencing. The mechanism used is basically the same as in HDLC, using the cyclic window technique. The first of the two numbering fields carries the number of the packet itself (P-send) and the second carries the acknowledgement number (P-received).

Data Sequencing

As the data field of any packet is of limited length a mechanism is provided by which strings of data which exceed this length may be logically connected. There are two reasons why this might occur:

- the user data file itself may exceed the maximum length of the data field in the network of origin;
- the data packet may pass between two networks, the second of which supports packets with a smaller maximum data field than the first. In this case the second network may have to segment the data of an incoming packet into two or more separate packets.

In either case use of the More Data Indication (M) is used. A packet with M set is said to be a category 2 packet and one with M clear is said to be a category 1 packet.

Category 1 Packets

- packets which do not have the local maximum data field length;

or:

— packets which do have the local maximum data field length and also have M clear.

Category 2 Packets

— packets which do have the local maximum data field length and also have M set.

Note that it is forbidden to set M if the local data field length is not fully utilised.

A 'packet sequence' is then defined as:

— a single category 1 packet;

or:

— any number of category 2 packets terminated by a category 1 packet.

Flow Control

Flow control in the data transfer mode makes use of the P (S) and P (R) fields as described above for packet sequencing.

Additionally, RR (Receive Ready) or RNR (Receive Not Ready) packets may be used for the carriage of acknowledgements when no data packets are available. The format of RR and RNR packets is given in Figure 6.15. Note that the use of the RR packet is not identical to the synonymous HDLC packet in that no poll/final bit feature is present.

RR is used to indicate that more data may be transmitted from the distant DTE. RNR is used to indicate a temporary inability to receive more data packets.

The function of each field should now be obvious to the reader. The coding of the identifier fields is as follows:

General Format Identifier:

0 0 0 1 for modulo 8 operation

0 0 1 0 for modulo 128 operation

Packet Type Identifier:

0 0 0 0 1 for RR packet

0 0 1 0 1 for RNR packet

Data packets are subject to the flow control mechanism described above. This allows both the network and the subscribers to regulate the rate at which the data packets on any virtual circuit may be transmitted and received. However, it is possible for the flow temporarily to dry up on a call. This blocks the passing of the very control information which may relieve the situation.

The user may therefore send an 'interrupt' packet, bearing the logical channel number of the virtual call, which will bypass all data packets in the network belonging to the call. This will be delivered to the distant DTE on the appropriate logical channel. The packet carries a single octet of user data which may be used to qualify the interrupt. The receiver must reply with an 'interrupt confirmation' packet before the network will accept the transmission of another interrupt on that virtual call.

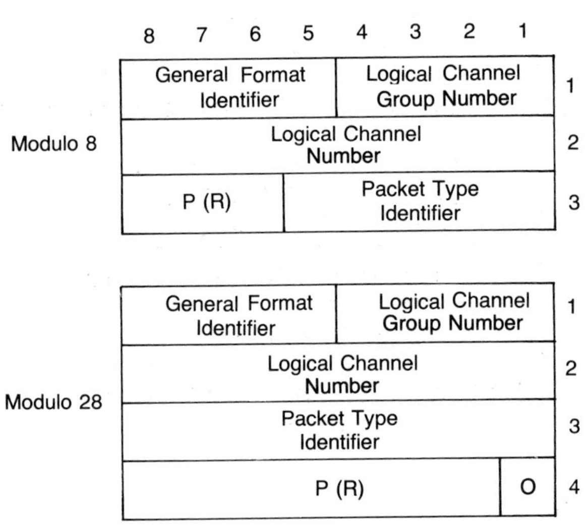

Figure 6.15 Structure of RR and RNR Packets

The format of the interrupt packet is given in Figures 6.16a and 6.16b. The coding of the fields is as follows:

General Format Identifier:

0 0 0 1 for modulo 8 operation

0 0 1 0 for modulo 128 operation

Packet Type Identifier:

0 0 1 0 0 0 1 1 interrupt packet

0 0 1 0 0 1 1 1 interrupt confirmation packet

User Data Field: contains one octet of user data which may be used to pass supervisory information from DTE to DTE.

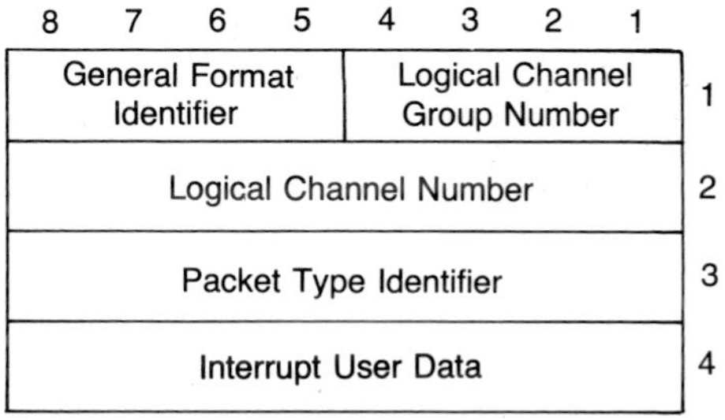

8 7 6 5	4 3 2 1	
General Format Identifier	Logical Channel Group Number	1
Logical Channel Number		2
Packet Type Identifier		3
Interrupt User Data		4

Figure 6.16a DTE and DCE Interrupt Packet Format

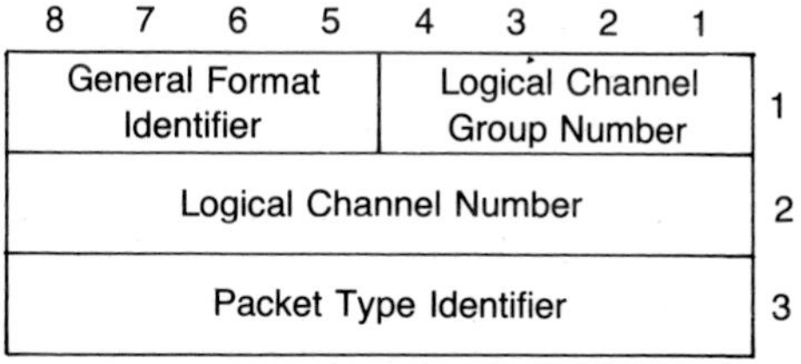

8 7 6 5	4 3 2 1	
General Format Identifier	Logical Channel Group Number	1
Logical Channel Number		2
Packet Type Identifier		3

Figure 6.16b DTE and DCE Interrupt Confirmation Packet Format

Call Termination

Either party may terminate a virtual call by sending a 'call clear request' packet, the network delivering a 'call clear indication' packet to the distant DTE. Again these two packets have the same format and contain complementary information. The structure of these packets is given in Figure 6.17. The coding of the fields is as follows:

General Format Identifier:

0 0 0 1 for modulo 8 operation

0 0 1 0 for modulo 128 operation

Packet Type Identifier:

0 0 0 1 0 0 1 1

Clearing Cause Field: indicates the reason for the clearing of a call. At the end of a successful data transfer session the clearing cause field will normally indicate a 'DTE originated' (either local or remote) clear.

Diagnostic Code Field: used to provide additional information about the reason for the clearing of a call. This is an optional field in the clear request packet but is mandatory in the clear indication packet. If not supplied with a clear request, the corresponding clear indication packet will contain all zeros in this field.

General Format Identifier	Logical Channel Group Number
Logical Channel Number	
Packet Type Identifier	
Clearing Cause	
Diagnostic Code	

Figure 6.17 Clear Request and Clear Indication Packet Format

The response to clear request and clear indication packets are DTE and DCE generated 'Clear Confirmation' packets. Their format is given in Figure 6.18. The coding of the general format field is:

0 0 0 1 for modulo 8 operation

0 0 1 0 for modulo 128 operation

Note that after issuing a clear request packet a DTE may still receive incoming packets before the clear confirmation is issued.

General Format Identifier	Logical Channel Group Number
Logical Channel Number	
Packet Type Identifier	

Figure 6.18 Clear Confirmation Packet

Terminal States

It can be seen that as the communication session progresses, the associated logical channels go through a number of distinguishable states. These states have been identified and named by CCITT (or rather misnamed as CCITT refers to DTE states when in fact they are generally referring to Logical Channel States as viewed by the DTE).

Figure 6.19 illustrates a data transfer session and the appropriate list of states. Other states will be introduced in the following sections.

ERROR CONTROL

A distinction should be made between an error (ie an unwanted deviation from normal procedure) and a negative response (an indication that a request cannot be serviced).

End to end transportation of the packet occurs in three stages:

— originating DTE to originating PSE;

— originating PSE to recipient PSE;

— recipient PSE to recipient DTE.

Each of these three stages should, in theory, provide reliable transportation of frames. However it is still possible for things to go wrong and hence some error control procedures are defined.

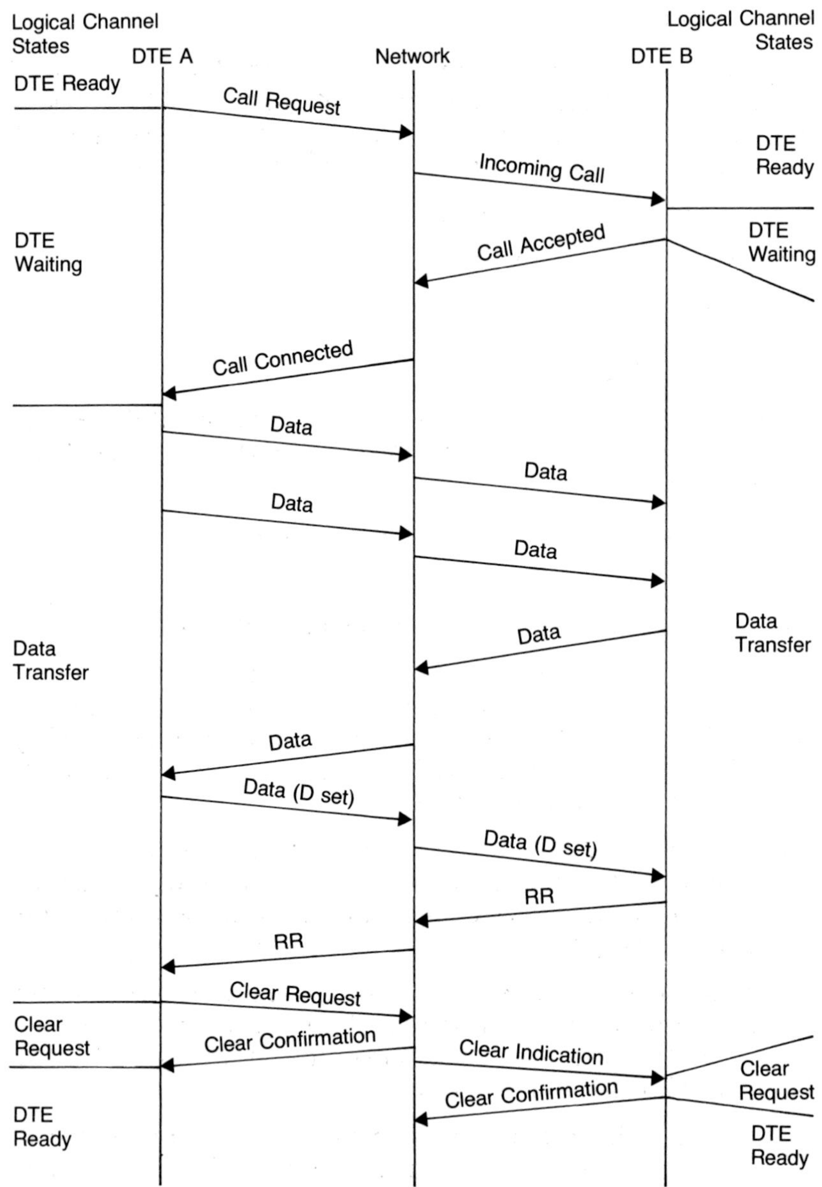

Figure 6.19 DTE States

Error Detection

Responsibility for the correctness of data in the level 3 packets is left entirely to the associated level 2 protocols and additionally to any higher-level validation procedures. However, three types of error may be detected by the level 3 protocol. These are:

— packet sequence number errors;

— illegal service request;

— illegal packet format.

Error Correction

If an erroneous, or ambiguous situation is encountered then the DTE may invoke error correction (or recovery) procedures at one of three levels:

— repeat erroneous and subsequent packets;

— reset logical channel;

— reset all logical channels associated with DTE.

The first option, used if an erroneous packet is received during an otherwise successful transmission, is to issue a 'DTE Reject' packet. This causes the PSE to retransmit the packet identified by the P (R) field and all subsequent packets. The format of the DTE REJ packet is given in Figure 6.20.

As the DTE REJ packet is only requesting a repeat of packets at the local end (PSE to DTE) it does not contain any diagnostic information nor does it require any response other than the requested packet(s).

The second method of error recovery is used when an erroneous situation occurs on a virtual circuit. It is then necessary to reset the virtual circuit to a predefined or 'initial' state. Both the P (S) and P (R) counters must be reset to 0.

This reset is indicated by the issue of a 'reset request' packet from a DTE or a 'reset indication' packet from a PSE. The format of these packets is given in Figure 6.21.

The coding of the fields is as follows:

General Format Identifier:

0 0 0 1 for modulo 8 operation

0 0 1 0 for modulo 128 operation

Reset Cause Field: indicates either that the reset is DTE requested or gives information of the reason for a network generated reset.

Diagnostic Code Field: an optional field in the reset request packet that may be used to provide further information concerning the cause of the reset.

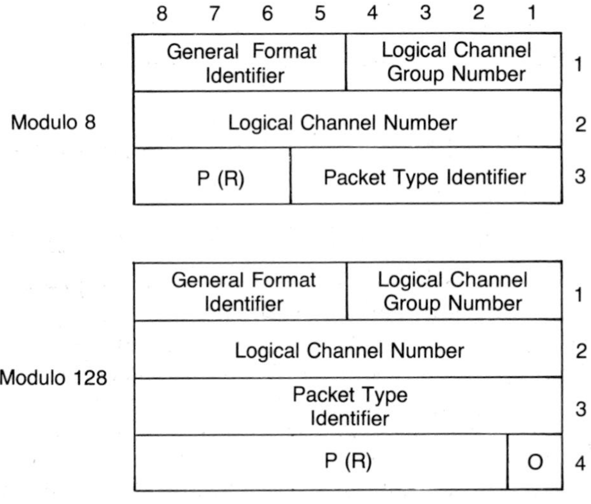

Figure 6.20 DTE REJ Packet

The response to a reset request or reset indication packet is provided, in both cases, by a 'reset confirmation' packet. The format of this packet is given in Figure 6.22. The coding of the general format identifier is as follows:

0 0 0 1 for modulo 8 operation

0 0 1 0 for modulo 128 operation

A DTE that issues a reset request packet has the appropriate logical channel placed in the 'DTE reset request' state until the reset confirmation packet is returned. At this point the logical channel returns to the 'Ready' state. A corresponding state of 'DCE restart request' is passed through by logical channels receiving a reset indication packet.

8 7 6 5	4 3 2 1	
General Format Identifier	Logical Channel Group Number	1
Logical Channel Number		2
Packet Type Identifier		3
Resetting Cause		4
Diagnostic Code		5

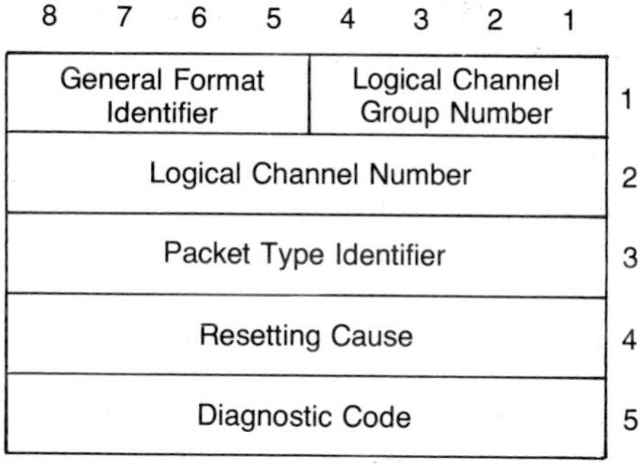

Figure 6.21 Reset Request and Reset Indication Packet Format

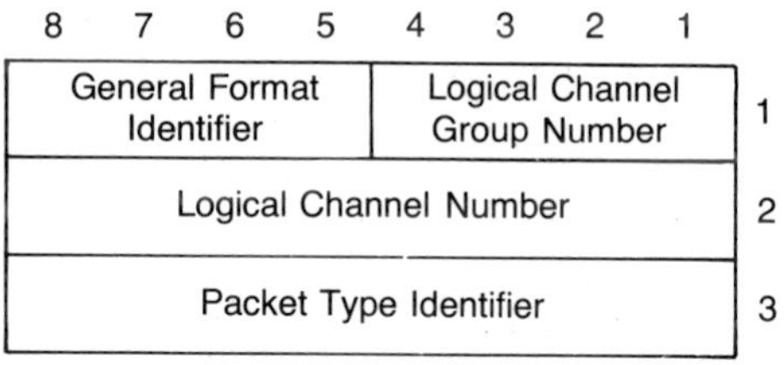

8 7 6 5	4 3 2 1	
General Format Identifier	Logical Channel Group Number	1
Logical Channel Number		2
Packet Type Identifier		3

Figure 6.22 DTE and DCE Reset Confirmation Packet Format

The third and most severe form of recovery is employed when a DTE or its PSE loses track of all logical channels. This is akin to losing the HDLC link between the two equipments and may be caused by such events as a power failure. A restart is requested by a DTE in a 'restart request' packet and by a DCE in a 'restart indication' packet. Confirmation of both these requests is given by a restart confirmation packet.

Figures 6.23 and 6.24 illustrate the structure of these packets. The coding of the fields is as follows:

General Format Identifier:

0 0 0 1 for modulo 8 operation

0 0 1 0 for modulo 128 operation

Logical Channel: set to all zeros.

Diagnostic Code Field: as in other supervisory packets this field is optional in DTE generated packets.

On issue, or receipt of a restart packet a DTE is placed in the 'restart request' state. Each logical channel then reverts to its ready state.

8	7	6	5	4	3	2	1	
General Format Identifier				0	0	0	0	1
0	0	0	0	0	0	0	0	2
1	1	1	1	1	0	1	1	3
Restarting Cause								4
Diagnostic Code								5

Figure 6.23 Restart Request and Restart Indication Packet Format

8	7	6	5	4	3	2	1	
General Format Identifier				0	0	0	0	1
0	0	0	0	0	0	0	0	2
1	1	1	1	1	1	1	1	3

Figure 6.24 Restart Confirmation Packet Format

OTHER MODES

The preceding sections have given a thorough description of operation under X.25 SVC procedures. There are however, three other modes of operation under X.25 procedures, these are:

— Permanent Virtual Circuit;

— Datagram;

— Fast Call Select;

Each of these is discussed briefly below.

Permanent Virtual Circuit (PVC)

A PVC operates in exactly the same way, using the same packets as an SVC. The difference between the two modes is that the VC of a PVC is, as its name suggests, of a permanent nature. The logical channels of a PVC are retained for exclusive use of that PVC. After resets a PVC returns to the Data Transfer state and call select and call clear functions are not used.

Datagram

The two modes of operation described above provide efficient operating procedures under two circumstances:

— large volumes of data are transferred during a virtual call;

— associations between terminals are of long duration.

Conversely, for small data volume, occasional connection, these methods are inefficient.

One solution to this problem is provided by the 'datagram' facility.

A datagram is a self-contained packet, carrying sufficient information to be routed from source to sink without a prior exchange of information. Datagrams are 'one off' packets and are treated as such by the network; ie if several datagrams are sent from one DTE to a single destination DTE delivery order is not guaranteed.

Indeed datagram delivery itself is not guaranteed and hence a datagram may be lost within the network.

Figure 6.25 illustrates the structure of a datagram packet.

The address and facility fields of a datagram packet are identical to those of a call request packet. The remainder of the datagram packet consists of the user-data field which has a standard maximum length of 128 octets. There are no optional maximum sizes and hence fragmentation of datagrams cannot occur.

The first two octets of the user-data field are reserved for a 'datagram identification' (DGID) which can be used to uniquely identify the packet associated with the destination address.

The response to a datagram comes in the form of a 'Datagram Service Signal' packet as shown in Figure 6.26. There are two classes of datagram service signal packet:

— datagram service signal – specific;

— datagram service signal – general.

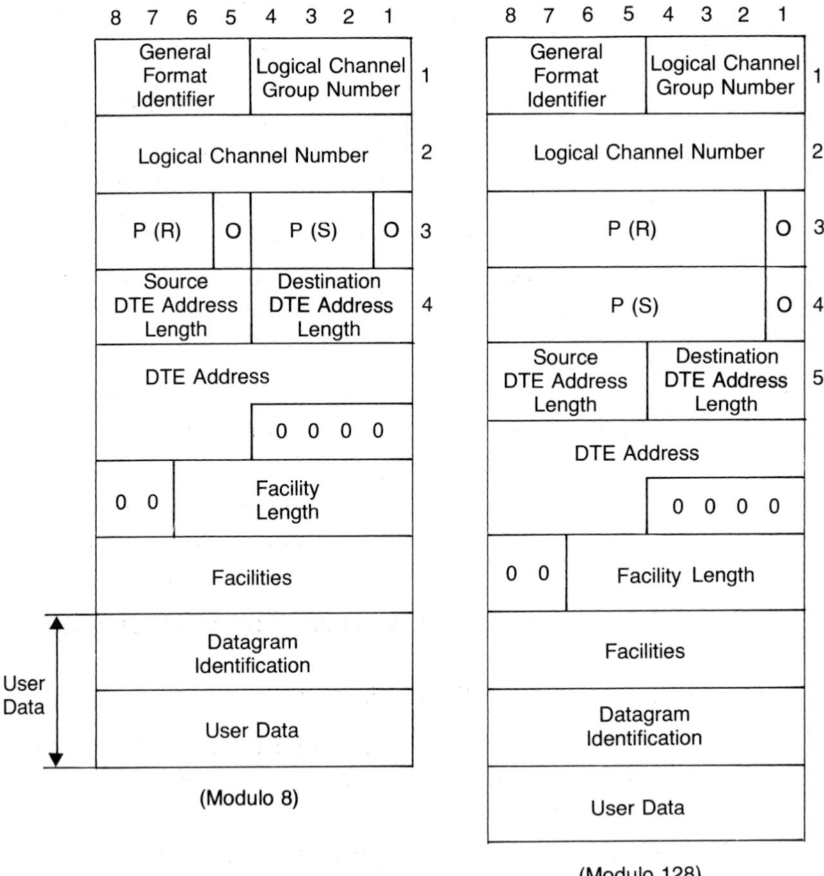

Figure 6.25 DCE and DTE Datagram Packet Format

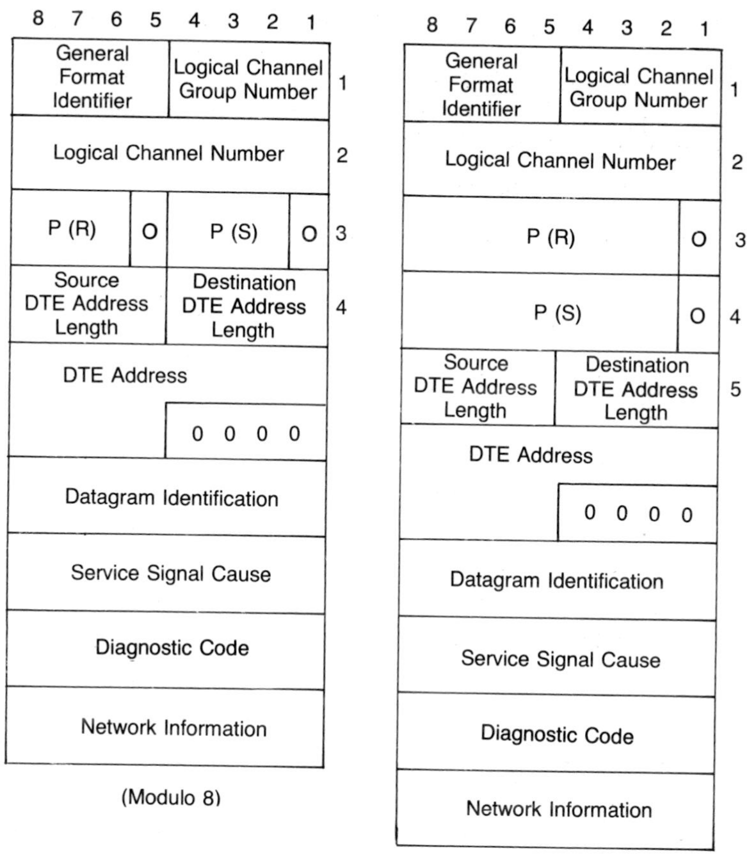

Figure 6.26 Datagram Service Signal Packet Information

The first of these has itself two classes:

— datagram rejected; indicating that the network has discarded the datagram due to some error or inconsistency in the datagram itself;

— delivery confirmation; an optional service which gives a positive indication that delivery has taken place. Note that the service signal packet retains the DGID field to indicate to the source, which datagram is being referred to.

The service signal – general may be sent by the network to indicate to a terminal that there is some change of status within the network which affects all datagrams. This, for example, provides a mechanism by which the network can exhibit flow control over the issue of datagrams from DTEs.

Fast Call Select

Implementation of the datagram service requires procedures which are significantly different to those of SVCs. Indeed the datagram service must be completed on dedicated logical channels which cannot be used for SVCs. An alternative approach for the requirements of transaction-processing applications is provided by the fast select facility.

The basis of this option is to allow up to 128 octets of user data to be included in the SVC call request packet. The recipient DTE responds to a fast select incoming call packet in one of two ways:

- an FS call accept packet, which again contains up to 128 octets of user data is returned. This establishes a conventional SVC;
- an FS call clear packet is returned containing up to 128 octets of data. This packet also terminates the call, making its use ideal for enquiry/response transactions.

The call request/incoming call and the call accept/call confirmation packets are similar for normal SVC and fast select connections. The only difference is that the length of the data field may be extended to include the additional data permitted under the FS option. The FS option is invoked by a request in the facilities field.

The FS facility clear request/clear indication packet format is a substantially enlarged version of the SVC clear request/clear indication packet. This is illustrated in Figure 6.27.

The sequence of packets for FS operation with immediate call clear is given in Figure 6.28.

As networks will often support only one of the datagram or fast select services, a procedure is defined by which a fast select from one network may be translated to a datagram within another and vice versa. The user is then not aware that communication is with a dissimilar service.

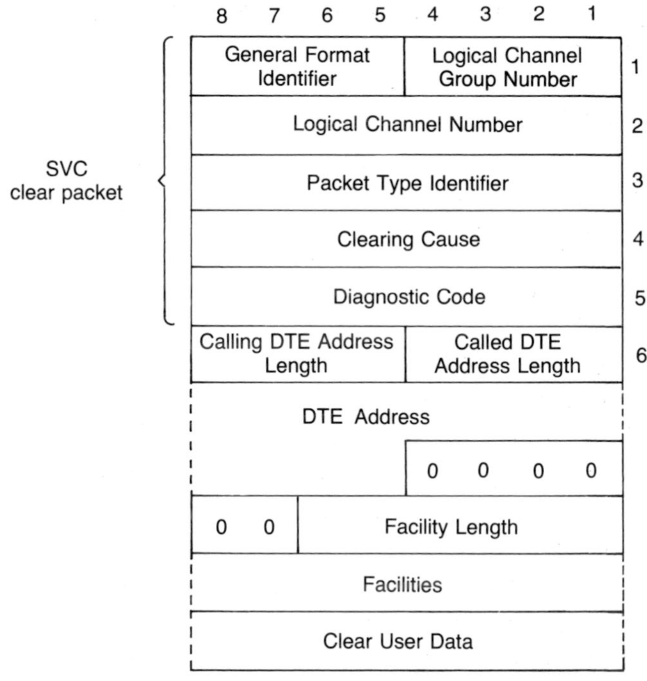

Figure 6.27 Clear Request/Clear Indication Packet Format (Fast Select)

IMPLEMENTING X.25

From the foregoing it will be appreciated that X.25 is not something that in all cases can be simply adopted and slotted into existing software and hardware. Indeed one can look upon a packet switching network and in particular the PAD facility as some kind of distributed front end. Ultimately systems will be purpose-designed to make maximum use of the technique and to achieve the efficiencies that it promises. In the meantime it is a question of adaptation of existing systems and this requires a compromise between cost and efficiency.

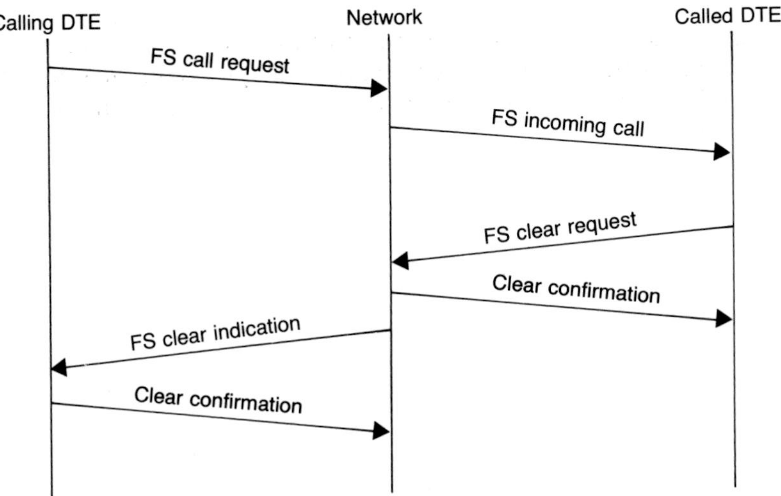

Figure 6.28 Fast-Select Operation

In some cases it may be possible to use the network transparently. For example, a remote job entry terminal previously working in block mode to a mainframe, could instead send and receive data blocks in native format but wrapped in packets. This implies either a minimum change to the existing hardware or software at both ends or perhaps the addition of a protocol convertor interposed between the subscriber and the network. Alternatively these convertors could be opaque to the native procedures behaving to each subscriber as if they were the thing at the other end. These kinds of *ad hoc* solutions are not always practicable if the parameters of the native protocols cannot be adjusted to work with the store-and-forward environment (even with short message transit times) of packet switching.

Futhermore with the advent of intelligent terminal systems that can emulate a range of proprietary terminals and their associated protocols, alternative solutions present themselves. One such is to use some standard procedure across the network agreed between all terminals and hosts. This is converted into the appearance expected by the mainframe computer by means of an emulation package running in the communications front end. This is in essence how the PAD facility functions, the procedure in question being the CCITT Recommendation X.29, supporting simple TTY devices.

7 Conclusions

This book has been designed to satisfy two objectives. These are:

— to provide the framework of a technique which can be used to evaluate the structure and operation of any protocol;

— to apply this technique to a selection of data communications protocols, thereby describing their structure and operation.

The effectiveness of the technique can be evaluated at two levels. The first is that it has proved to be a suitable tool for describing those protocols to which it has been applied in this text. The second will be verified if the reader applies the technique to other protocols.

It is traditional to include in the conclusions of a book such as this, some prediction as to further developments. Despite the apparent stability of some of the protocols described, there are many developments in the field of data communication protocols which may be predicted with an acceptable degree of certainty.

The first prediction is that specific protocols will fit more precisely into the various reference models. Hence data communication protocols will be concerned with the transfer of bit-strings only. No structuring of the information fields will be enforced, neither will any interpretation of their content be specified.

Secondly, the techniques described will be applied to many more technologies than those to which they are traditionally accustomed. Examples of this can already be seen in such cases as the use of HDLC-based protocols for local area networks.

Finally, the increased functionality of traditional networks will require the definition and implementation of many more optional features. Facility negotiation at call set up time will become of much more widespread concern.

Glossary

Acknowledgement (ACK) A control character used to acknowledge the correct receipt of a message.

Adaptive Routeing A routeing system in which the network may alter the route to suit the current requirements of the network or user.

Alphabet A limited set of characters used to transmit information.

Application A job or task that can be performed by a computer.

Application Program or Software A set of computer instructions which are executed by the computer to perform some task directly associated with an application.

Architecture A framework for a computer system which defines its functions, interfaces and procedures.

Asynchronous An event is asynchronous if it occurs at a time which is not related to the timing of another event.

Asynchronous Transmission Transmission for which the start of a character can occur at any time after completion of the previous character. Also referred to as stop/start transmission.

Automatic Retransmission on Request (ARQ) An error correcting system by which the receiver of certain corrupted messages may request and receive a retransmission of the corrupted message.

Bit Abbreviation of Binary Digit. Smallest unit of information in computer system.

Bit Stripping Removal of bits inserted into a message under bit stuffing system.

Bit Stuffing Insertion of additional bits into a message so that a certain pattern of bits may be avoided. Used to distinguish between user information and control information.

Block A group of characters transmitted as a unit.

Buffer A device used for temporary storage of information.

Byte A group of bits of specified length (usually eight bits).

CCITT (Commite Consultatif International Telegraphique et Telephonique The international body through which the national telecommunications bodies co-ordinate their activities.

Character Letter, figure, number or other sign contained in a message.

Check Bit/Byte A bit, byte or character which carries parity information.

Circuit Switching A method of connecting together two users of a telecommunications service which allocates a circuit for their exclusive use for the duration of the call.

Code — A method of representing each of a number of values (or symbols) as a particular arrangement (or sequence) of discrete conditions or events.

Contention — A 'dispute' between several devices for the use of a shared facility.

Control Character — A character which conveys system information.

Datagram — A single packet, in a packet switched network, which is routed without reference by the network to any other packet being sent.

DCE (Data Circuit-terminating Equipment) — A CCITT term which denotes the equipment which terminates the PTT-supplied circuit. Used colloquially to refer to any communications device which connects to a data terminal.

Distributed Computing — A system in which there are several autonomous but interacting processors and/or data stores at different geographical locations.

DTE (Data Terminal Equipment) — A CCITT term which denotes the customer equipment which is connected to a DCE. Used colloquially to refer to any communicating terminal equipment.

Duplex Transmission — Transmission in both directions, simultaneously.

Echoplex — Return by the receiver of a character from an input keyboard to the printer associated with that keyboard.

Emulation — Making one device act as and hence be treated as another.

End User — The person or device which uses an information processing system.

Error Correcting Code A data transmission (or other) code by which some errors which may be introduced during transmission may be both detected and corrected.

Error Detecting Code A data transmission (or other) code by which some errors which may be introduced during transmission may be detected but not corrected.

Error Rate The ratio of the number of elements received, to the total number of elements sent.

File An organised collection of information.

Flow Control The mechanism by which the rate of data exchange may be controlled.

Frame A group of bits transmitted as a unit.

Full Duplex Transmission As duplex transmission.

Half Duplex Transmission A transmission system in which information may flow in both directions but not simultaneously.

High Level Data Link Control (HDLC) A protocol designed for data transmission, which does not use control characters and is data independent.

Intelligent Terminal A communicating terminal capable of performing additional functions such as data storage or emulation.

Interface A boundary between two devices across which the form and functions of the signals which pass through it are specified.

International Organisation for Standardisation (ISO) The body which exists to promote the development of standards in the world. Membership consists of national organisations which are representative bodies of standards within their country.

Layer — A set of logically related functions which are grouped together. Interfaces to and from the layer can be standardised but not the ways the internal functions are performed.

Leased Circuit — A telephone or telegraph line or channel leased from a carrier company for dedicated use by the lessee. The specifications of the circuit performance are listed by the supplier.

Link — The communications facility that interconnects two DCEs.

Logical Connection — A connection in which the means of information transfer may not exist as a real physical entity for the duration of the call.

Message — A logically related connection of data to be moved.

Message Switching — A method of establishing communications in a switched network: a message is received at a central location, stored temporarily until the proper outgoing line is available, then transmitted to the appropriate destination.

Modem — A device used to convert (modulate) serial digital data from a transmitting terminal to a signal suitable for transmission over a telephone channel, and then to reconvert the signal (demodulate) back to serial digital data for acceptance by the receiving terminal.

Multiplexing — Use of a single channel to transport more than one stream of information.

Multipoint Circuit — A communications network of leased circuits in which information from a single central node is transferred simultaneously to a number of remote nodes. Information transmitted from any remote node is received only by the central node, there are no facilities for direct communication between remote nodes.

Negative Acknowledgement (NAK) — A control character used to indicate that an incorrect message has been received.

Node — A focal point in a communications network.

Open Systems Interconnection (OSI) — Standardised procedures for the exchange of information between terminals, computers, people, networks, etc which are accessible to one another by virtue of their mutual use of these procedures.

Packet — A group of bits including a destination address transmitted as a single unit over a packet switched network.

Packet Interleaving — A technique of multiplexing in a packet switch environment whereby the packets from each sub-channel are multiplexed together.

Packet Switching — A term used for a data transmission network which is designed to carry data in the form of packets. The data, in packets, is passed to the network, and devices within it use the control information to transmit the packet to the correct address.

Parallel Transmission — The simultaneous transmission of the bits making up a character.

Parity A technique used to help detect data transmission errors: a non-information bit is added to a character so that the resulting number of 1s in the group is odd (odd parity) or even (even parity).

Polling A method of controlling terminals in a multipoint or clustered data network where each terminal is interrogated in turn by the computer to determine its status, ie when it is ready to transmit or receive data.

Port The channel on a computer or front end processor to which I/O devices are connected.

Protocol A set of rules to ensure a meaningful communication between co-operating partners.

PTT (Post, Telegraph and Telephone administration) A general term to denote a supplier of telecommunications services.

Public Data Network A communications system which is intended for transmission of digital data and which is available to anyone wishing to subscribe to it.

Redundant Code A technique whereby data bits are added to the transmitted message for error checking purposes. These bits are redundant in the sense that they do not carry information.

Residual Error Rate The ratio of the number of bits, characters or blocks incorrectly received (but undetected or uncorrected by the error control equipment) to the total number of bits, characters or blocks sent.

Routeing The function of selecting the path for transmission of data within a network.

Satellite Processor A computer system which has a subsidiary role in a distributed system.

Serial Transmission A method of data transfer in which the bits of a character are sequentially transmitted.

Session When two software users' resources or other components in a network are connected together for the purpose of exchanging information they are said to be in session.

Simplex Transmission A protocol or facility that supports communications in one direction only.

Switching In computer or communications networks, switching is the process by which services or data are directed to the appropriate user.

Synchronous Transmission A transmission technique in which an uninterrupted block of data is sent, with each block preceded by one or more synchronising characters to synchronise the receiver with the incoming data.

Time Division Multiplexing (TDM) A system that allocates the usage of a transmission circuit amongst a number of channels by dividing the usage into time slots.

Terminal A device for sending and/or receiving data on a communications channel.

Transaction Processing The entering of records of events into information processing systems as each event occurs.

Transparent A communications link is said to be

transparent when it does not alter in any way the contents of the message it transmits.

Virtual Circuit
A call using a virtual current uses real physical connections which the transmission service may employ for other calls made by other subscribers.

V-Series (CCITT)
The CCITT recommendations for data transmission over telephone (ie analogue) networks.

X-Series (CCITT)
The CCITT recommendations for data transmission over digital data networks.

Index